P.I.G.S.

This book is dedicated to all the Indian graduate students who came to the land of opportunities to only find themselves between a lot of fellow countrymen, bed bugs and tons of girls they are never going to get with, well most of them at least.

P.I.G.S.

By

Anish Sadanandan

Expression Publications

ISBN – 819059197-5

Published by

Expression publications

B/3, Aniket so-1, Bibawewadi Area,
Pune- 411037. Maharashtra.

Published by
SHREE BOOK CENTRE
8 Kakad Industrial Estate, S. Keer Road (Off.L.J. Road), Matunga (West)
MUMBAI 400 016 (India) Tel : 24377516/24374559 Telefax : 91-22-24309183
E-mail : sales@shreebookcentre.com

A lot of Indian movie directors or music directors are usually "inspired" by some other movie or by some tune. So following in that tradition, I will say I am inspired by all those writers whose books I have read, and I am going to begin with a quote just like many of them do. And I am going to quote the best:

> *"What goes around comes around"*   - Justin Timberlake

Also, I have to quote the whole nation, my motherland:

> *"You are either a doctor or an engineer, or you are nothing"*
- Indian parents

TERMINOLOGY

Before you delve into the book, I think you should be familiar with some terms that you will come across in this book.

Desi - Literal meaning is someone from your own country, though it is usually used for Indians only.

ABCD - I am not talking about the Kal Penn movie here. ABCD stands for American Born Confused Desi. An Indian born and raised in America. Confused because while they are mingling with their friends in a western cultural background, their parents constantly remind them that they have to find a nice Indian boy/girl to marry. So a half of them are western while the other half is on the brown lookout, a very dangerous combination.

FOB - Fresh of the boat. Now *FOB*s and ABCDs are arch enemies. The fobby guys are totally into *ABCD* chics, something I personally never understood. I suppose it is because these girls know how to carry themselves (desi girls take notes), and also the accent is somehow a turn on for most guys. I think all these guys see a Priya Rai in every *ABCD* girl. The mutual hate arises because these girls hate being hit on by a *FOB* (apparently we are not cool enough), which of course makes the guys think these chics are full of it, and of course if a girl doesn't like you, she is a bitch. The fobby girls hate

*ABCD*s because, well they do not get any attention from the *ABCD* guys, and their only chance on getting laid, the fobby guys, are busy drooling over those "bitches".

Just to clarify, this book is not about the ongoing war between FOBs and ABCDs. It is about my life in India and my experiences as a graduate student.

Introduction

I think the most apt way to begin this book is to tell you why it is named P.I.G.S. I remember when my parents were persuading my brother to stay in India and not go to the USA for his masters, my dad tried every trick in the book but I thought the most outrageous one was when he said, "Do you know what they call Indian graduate students in US? They call them P.I.G.S., Poor Indian Graduate Students." At the time, I couldn't stop laughing. You are talking about a country here that has never discriminated based on race, religion, or color. A country where George Bush Jr. was president for 8 long years, where the winner of a championship game between any two American teams are called the "World Champions", where the ground floor is called the first floor though it is at ground level. They are most normal people around; at least that is what I thought.

Instead of diving right into my graduate life, I would like to go a bit into my past so that you know why I am a douchebag that I am now. My name is Anish Sadanandan. I did my B.E. in Production Engineering from Mumbai University, and just graduated with a M.S. in Engineering Management. The more intricate details you will learn through the course of this book. Now to tell you a bit about my wonderful life.

The wonder years

I have a lot of things I should thank my parents for. To begin with, I am thankful that though being from South India, Kerala to be precise, they decided to move to Mumbai and raise my brother Ashish and me there. Don't get me wrong, I am very proud to be a Keralite, but if I were born and raised there, I would now have a mustache (considered sexy down there), a nice big rounded belly (apparently the more the surface area the better), and a side parting hairstyle with enough oil on it to cook food for the entire Vatican City. During my undergraduate years, I actually put on a lot of weight and was around 100 kgs. And at this healthiest point of my life, we visited my relatives in Kerala. Undoubtedly, I was the hottest property down south after gaining that much weight. My aunts said I had never looked better, and that I would get the most beautiful girls there for marriage. Though that thought made me think twice before shedding some kilos, I did manage to lose around 20 kgs before our next trip to God's Own Country the following year, but this time around I was destined to get proposals from the bottom of the pile. Health is wealth takes a back seat here to heavier the sexier, evidently.

Another thing I should thank my parents for is putting me in an English medium school. India has about 29 spoken languages, and each language could be the primary language in schools. In Mumbai, Hindi, Marathi, Gujarati and English medium schools were the forerunners, and English medium school was where my folks thought it would be the best for us.

I personally believe it was good because today I can converse well with people from different countries in English without having any glitches, apart from the accent which might be tough to understand at times (once I had to say porn 10 times before putting it as pornographic videos for the other person to understand what I was talking about). BUT in the end my parents are human too, and to err is human and to forgive is divine. However, I will never forgive them for putting me in a Sikh school. See, once upon a time, a very important person to the Sikhs was kidnapped. To rescue him, the Sikhs made a plan to attack at midnight. At the stroke of midnight, they yelled out *"bole so nihal, sat sri akal"* and rescued their leader by absolutely demolishing the kidnappers*. However, from that day onwards, people believed that Sikhs completely lose it at midnight. Over the years, this time changed from 12am to 12pm, I suppose because kids couldn't tease other kids at midnight, they thought noon would be a better option. Also, going to Guru Harkrishan High School meant that every student of that school went bonkers at noon, not just the Sikh students, everyone! So you can imagine the amount of ridicule I had to face from friends outside of school.

In India, as everyone knows, arranged marriage within castes is a prominent ritual. So all these little Sikh kids running around with their small turbans knew they were going to get some hot women as wives. As a result of this knowledge, if any kid from a different caste would try to flirt with any of these gorgeous women, these little turban wearing punks would give them a smug smile which pretty much said, "Try all you want but in the end one of us is going to tap that". It was like keep a box

---

* *This story needs to be clarified as it was told to me by a Sikh friend after 12pm.*

full of candy in front of a child, and then telling him it was forbidden. This made us non-Sikhs really aggravated and we did what we could do best, make more fun of those pompous pricks.

Like every other school, we had nicknames for most of the teachers as well. Hindi teacher who slept through most of the class was *sleeping beauty*, science teacher who had a tendency to let one rip once in a while was *gas cylinder*, another Hindi teacher who kind of resembled a bulldog, well she was *bulldog* of course, teacher named Mr. De Gama was *Vasco De Gama*, and so on and so forth. We had some weird teachers too. Apart from *sleeping beauty* and *gas cylinder*, we had a geography teacher who would call every guy "poppy" for some reason. I don't know what exactly it meant, maybe we knew we would be smoking some derivatives of poppy seeds some time in our lives, or maybe he just loved poppy seeds so much that he called all the kids in his class poppy. Now that I think about it, he reminds me a lot of Mr. Garrison from South Park. This teacher even used to run his hands on the backs of his favorite male students in a circular motion. Now I know what you must be thinking, Mr. Garrison, running hands on the back of young boys, I used to think on those lines too but can you imagine my surprise when he got married? It was definitely a big shocker. In the end, I guess he was just a very friendly teacher who looked after his best students.

I am sure a lot of you might be feeling disappointed right now, considering that the geography teacher didn't turn out to be a pervert, and it is always fun to read about one. Well I wouldn't want to disappoint you. I have some personal experiences on those fronts too. I played field hockey as a goalkeeper, a very bad goalie at that. I really don't even want to start on the margins with which we lost most of our games. One day when I was changing, the coach comes into the room, and suddenly tells me to wear an abdomen guard (a cup) to protect my "goods". This seems like a normal thing of course but he was holding my crotch the whole time while saying this! If there are any shrinks reading this, they might try to analyze my character based on this, but you can be rest assured that this did not affect me in anyway. I was always able to joke about it, and I still can. Coming back to the pervert, he did this a couple of times and I was a bit more taken aback the second time. As a 6th grader who wants to be in the team, you wouldn't say no to the coach but I spoke to a couple of teammates and he had done this to them too. After he tried this trick on one of the 9th graders in the team, the student wrote a letter to the principal explaining what the coach has been up to with much exaggerated statements like, "He uses socks as condoms". I didn't understand how a sock would work as a condom anyway. But the letter worked, and the freak was fired. Surprisingly no legal action was taken. All the hockey players had reason to believe he went all the way with one of the players, a very cute Sikh boy. During one of the practice sessions, this player made a lot of mistakes and so the coach sent him into the school to the top floor, and then in some time ended the practice early and sent us all home, while the boy was upstairs and the coach went up to join him. The next day the Sikh kid wasn't walking properly*. Hmmm, I

*This was mostly a rumor but story of a guy get nailed in the ass by the coach was priceless.

wonder why?

I think all the teachers contributed to me having a fun-filled school experience. If it weren't the slapping incident, it would be one teacher crying because some other teacher said something to him/her. Or, it would be one teacher bitching to all the students about how she should be given the responsibility of managing all the class monitors and prefects, and not the new teacher in school. All in all, school life was filled with drama, just like a Bollywood movie, the very stuff that inspires every Indian. Where would we Indians be without Bollywood?

Considering my qualifications now, you might think that I was one of the nerds in school, with glasses and braces, not really into sports and could not speak to girls if my life dependent on it. *Au contraire,* I was anything but all of those things. I was into every sport possible. I represented the school in football, cricket (I am Indian, I have to play cricket), basketball, volleyball, handball, table tennis, badminton, field hockey and athletics. My parents were really proud of my sporting achievements, considering my brother was everything I described earlier; summing him up in school in one word, geek. I was known well amongst teachers and students because of sports, however, it only got me attention from the not-so-good looking female crowd and I think this had a lot to do with me having no idea of how to carry myself with some swagger, or carry myself at all for that matter. Am I glad that changed over time?

"How will you learn to rise up without falling?", "Failure is only a step towards success". I am sure all of us are familiar with these words of wisdom, but we the proud athletes of Guru Harkrishan High School heard this after every game. We sucked in every sport. We might end up with one victory in a season, which would be caused by the other team not showing up, or some other miracle, but if we ever got a victory on the sheets, it would spark wild celebrations.

After all, we only got to do that once or twice a year. Out of all the teams, I would have to say the football team was the funniest. Though I had good skills with the ball (I am a good football player now, for the record), the coach decided to make me goalie because I was one of the tallest kids in the team. I didn't object as I just loved the sport and wanted to be a part of the team. As if that wasn't bad enough, he decided to make some Sikh boys defenders. Why would you make kids with turbans defenders? In each game we had one of them head the ball, only to have their turban removed, and so they would have to go to the sidelines to tie back the small little thing which took at least 15-20 minutes, meaning we would be down by a man for that time. During one of the games, a winger from the other team ran down our left flank and crossed the ball. One of our brave Sikh defenders jumped up into the air and caught the ball with his hands. Yes, he caught the ball*. Of course the other team got a penalty, which I was unable to save. I wouldn't want to put all the blame on my defenders though. I was most certainly one of the worst goalies the sport had ever seen.

I distinctly remember one particular game against St. Francis D'Assisi, one of the best football schools in the city. It was a rainy day, and there was muck all over the ground, including the penalty area. Considering that they were one of the best

*I think it was after 12pm.

teams and we were the worst, it wasn't surprising when they took, if my memory serves me right, an 8-0 lead at half time. They continued scoring in the second half as well, with even their goalkeeper substituting as an outfield player to grab a brace himself. In a field where there was hardly a dry spot, including the penalty box, and with so many balls covered with mud flying past me into the net, my jersey was spotless, clean as a whistle. For one of the goals, the ball went past me at a distance at which a small dive would have been sufficient to make the save but I chose not to. One of the defenders asked me why I didn't dive for that ball, and I believe my exact words were, "I might get hurt if I dive". The final score of the game was 17-0. After these outstanding performances, the coach was replaced, and the new guy was the athletics coach, Mr. Ghodke, who didn't even know the rules of football. I convinced him I was an outfield player and a guy named Farid was made our goalie.

I can go on for a very long time about the failures of the different teams I played for in school, like when we went to play our first ever basketball game, and we lost the game with the final score being 4-2. No there is no typo there; they scored two baskets, while we had one. I really hope that the school's sports program has come a long way since I graduated.

Every school has one or two nice girls, nice because they sleep around with most of the guys. I wouldn't want to call them sluts and insult them, after all a lot of us gained invaluable experience from these promiscuous women. Our school wanted to one up every other school in each and every department. So even in this regard, instead of having a couple of "nice" girls, we had at least one in each batch. Our batch had three, out of which two were sisters. Of course, though being a bit easy, they were picky too. They wouldn't let the biggest losers (well all of us were losers) touch them. Had to be someone smart or someone good looking. Though I was smart, I somehow never had the courage to go up to one of them, and I guess I thought it was wrong to an extent. But there was this one moment that changed my take on this issue. There was a guy called Saj, a good-looking kid, who was actually a senior but had failed and had to repeat a year. One day, he was sitting behind one of the sisters in one class, and I was sitting in the adjacent row, in the same line of benches as them. In the middle of the lecture, I could hear giggles from behind me, and a friend sitting behind taps me on shoulder and asks to look at Saj. The guy was listening to the lecture with both his hands grasping the girl's frontal attractions from behind. Being one of the good students in the class, the first thing I thought of was, "How in the world is he concentrating on the lecture in that position?" Of course, I realized that focusing on the lecture was the least of his worries, and he was having a much better time than I ever did. That was the day I decided to take a stand on this issue, and make sure every guy has the right to enjoy lectures like that. A few days after that, I walked up to the other sister after school and told her I wanted to talk to her. We walked a bit, trying to get away from civilization as I knew it, and then I just turned and kissed her, and she didn't pull away either. This was my first ever kiss, and man did it feel good*. Of course, I had a boner from that moment, sometime in the afternoon, till I went to sleep at night. Every

*My first girlfriend is going to kill me if she reads this because she still thinks she was the first girl I ever kissed.

evening I went outside to play with friends, and that day I decided to wear a cup, just in case. There were many similar moments to follow after that but that was definitely the most memorable one.

Being involved in so many sports, and being one of the toppers in school, it was a surprise to a lot of people that I would get sent to the principal's office quite often. I was even sent to the principal's office once for calling a particular teacher a "mofo", and someone ratted me out. The teacher was standing next to me in the principal's office and crying. Can you imagine the feeling I got as a 12/13 yr old to have made a teacher cry? It was the proudest moment of my school days.

At that age, kids are always very impressionable and find the smallest of things very cool. One day, my brother took a sharpie (sketch pen) and put it at the center of the ceiling fan and slowly moved it to the periphery of the fan, making beautiful concentric circles in the process which looked stunning when the fan was rotating. This really inspired me to do this in class. The next day I went to school with just one thing in mind. As soon as the first class got over, I decorated the fan as planned. The other kids looked at it with astonishment, it was beautiful. I realized that I would get into trouble if I let it remain, so I took a wet cloth and erased the artwork. However, kids were a bit more impressed than I anticipated. Once the next class got over, they decided to do the same, but with ballpoint pens this time, which is of course next to impossible to erase from most surfaces. The teacher came in and saw the fans and asked who is responsible for it, and of course, like the good friends they were, everyone pointed towards me. I was asked to sit outside the classroom for three days unless my parents paid Rs.200 per fan to restore them. My dad just sent a letter to the principle saying, "We pay a lot of fees to the school anyway. I'm sure my son will enjoy the time outside class". My father knew me very well I suppose because I definitely enjoyed my three days out of class.

In India, not many folks have a sex talk with their kids. As a matter of fact, I personally don't know a single child who received sex education of any sort from their parents. The closest to that would be the parents giving a book to their children. Some schools would have a sex education lecture where the teacher would come in and ask if the students had any question, wait for a response which usually never came because the students would be too shy to ask anything, and then would say good and continue with history or geography. This lack of knowledge led to a lot of misconceptions and myths, like if the girl doesn't bleed the first time she has sex she is not a virgin, or if the girl blows into your penis while giving you a head, you could die, or my personal favorite which was told to me by a friend that after sex you have to leave the penis inside the vagina for a good few hours for every drop of sperm to fall in. This guy either had a lot of sperm or just wanted to make sure he got every girl he ever slept with pregnant. Mr. Dias wanted to change this tradition. He wanted to make sure every student passing out of GHK High School knew about sex.

These classes would start with him walking into the class with lot of charts and pictures; he would even draw diagrams on the board, fascinating diagrams if I may add. Most of the pictures even turned some guys on I think. There were some weird questions asked too, like how many times do you have to have sex before getting pregnant. I suppose reproduction was a main concern for the students, after all, with only the second largest population in the world, we had to close in on the number one spot and that huge responsibility was on our young shoulders. As an aftermath of the sex-ed, Mr. Dias even organized an AIDS awareness lecture, presented by two college students from a nearby girls' college. Yes, girls' college. Oh did I mention the two girls who came to our class were hot too? I still remember one of the girl's name was Sonal. Aaah Sonal! The whole purpose of AIDS awareness was moot considering that the only thing all the guys had in their heads was to do it with any one of them, with protection being our last concern of course. What else would you expect when two 18/19 yr old gorgeous women talk to 13 yr old boys? All of us asked the most nonsensical questions ever asked by mankind just to talk to them. Mine were, "Why don't sex workers get AIDS?", and, "Does AIDS spread via water?" I knew the answers too but who cared, an 18 yr old girl just spoke to me. After the awareness lecture, the girls were swarmed by the guys like bees over honey. One of my friends said his life was just made because his hand brushed Sonal's thigh. To be young again, and have these little things in life give you those pleasures. I doubt even actual sex would have given my friend that excitement he had that day. Some things are just priceless.

School always has crazy rumors flying around, a lot of them. Our school had its fair share too. From having lesbian teachers, to girls being pregnant, I had heard them all. New girls and guys in school were always a hot topic of discussion.

There was this one particular new girl who caught my eye. I don't know if I have ever told you guys this but I have a thing for dusky women, not that fair ones are unattractive, but if given a choice, I would always pick the dusky one. This new girl, Vedika, was dusky, intelligent and pretty good at sports too. She might not have been the best looking girl around but she had almost everything I was looking for in a woman. And did I mention she was well endowed too? All these things about her really attracted me towards her, and a lot of other guys. But she didn't really notice me, or refused to acknowledge me. I was not the most popular guy in school, neither was I the most good looking one, but I was good at sports, good at studies, pretty decent looking and was six feet tall in high school. That has to count for something.

Apparently, it didn't. Though through school years my self-confidence wasn't at its peak, my ego was still hurt by this newbie ignoring me. I know how the ladder system works. If a person above you on the ladder hits on you, you do not look away. How in the world was she looking away from me? As a young boy, the first thing guys do to hit on girls is, be rude to them, be as mean as possible and I did the same. "Dude what is with your last name? Why is it so weird?"*. However, it wasn't working, as a matter of fact, she had started resenting me. So I turned to plan B. I showed her my caring, sweet side. I would be as nice as possible, completely downplaying myself at every opportunity and as a prefect I would even take care of the 2nd graders, the class I was assigned to, and play with them a lot so that she could see how much I loved kids. And this tactic

*Imagine a guy who uses his dad's name as his last name saying that.

started working.

We both started calling each other after school, talking about our day though we were in the same class, bitching about others; it was the start of what is universally known as puppy love. But like any other love story, there had to be a villain, and in our story, it was a teacher. This teacher thought that a friend of mine and I would talk too much in class. So, she decided that we should be in different classes, and as a result, I was transferred to Div A. This was no upgrade of any sort, each grade was split into two divisions, A and B, and the students were randomly assigned to each class. However, I didn't want to leave my division because all my friends were in that class and also the girl I really liked; but I had to. For some reason, this minor separation caused a major setback in my chances with Vedika. We stopped talking frequently, no more phone calls, if we ran into each other in the hallways; we would just smile at each other. Everything went pretty much downhill. But come 10th grade, our final year in GHK high school and things were destined to change.

In 10th grade, I started talking to this friend of Vedika's, Anu. Anu used to live in the same apartment complex as Vedika. I have no recollection of how I started talking to her, but it was a good move to say the least. She started giving me all the inside information about Vedika, and what I should do to impress her, and I followed her lead. It worked to perfection, and one day Anu told me that Vedika was waiting for me to ask her out. This was the moment I had been waiting for, I was in! I just had to play it cool and tell her how I felt and we would be officially dating. So I conjured up all my guts, and called her that fateful Sunday afternoon. My folks were taking in nap in the hall for some reason, and my brother was in the bedroom we shared. So I decided to go in the balcony and talk to her. And if my mother decided to eavesdrop, which she often did when I was on the phone talking in English*, she could have heard every word I said. Luckily, she was fast asleep. I called Vedika and started making small talk. Then as I mustered up some courage I thought I should tell her how I felt. And I did it, I told her, "I love you". Yes I said I love you. You know why? Bollywood! I blame it completely on stupid Indian heroes using those three magical words every time in every movie. There was nothing like I like you or, I have feelings for you, or would you like to go out with me? There was just I love you. I did watch Hollywood movies too, but in those movies the guy usually ended up kissing the girl, or vice versa. That is a big no no in India. Physical activities were reserved for after marriage, at least that was the unwritten rule, but as we all know rules were meant to be broken. Anyway, so I said those words and was waiting for an answer, and in typical Hindi movie fashion she replied by saying the same three words back. If at that moment someone asked me the definition of love, they would have got the weirdest answer ever imaginable. Either of us, I'm sure, didn't know the meaning of love, we had an infatuation and that had to be love from what we knew. And that was how my first relationship began.

For some reason, I was transferred back to Div B in 10th grade, and it worked perfectly for us. The last few months in school we would be in the same class, sitting very close to each other, talking whenever we got the opportunity, it was just

*English meant I'm talking to girls, while Hindi was reserved for guys.

perfect. We had small fights too, and whenever we fought, I would call her and just not talk. So it was a blank call where she knew it is me but not a single word out of my mouth. I really have no clue what I was trying to achieve by that. Was I giving her the silent treatment after I screwed up? Though it doesn't make sense, it somehow always worked. She would think I am feeling too guilty to talk which I was, and after a few of these blank calls, she would be fine again.

There was this other guy in class, Micky, who liked Vedika too. Though no one in school knew about us dating, everyone kind of had an idea, and Micky was the one worst affected by it. Days when Vedika and I would have a fight and give each other the cold shoulder, he would be the happiest guy in class, talking to her at every opportunity. And as soon as we would make up, he would be more depressed than Shah Rukh Khan in *Kabhi Khushi Kabhi Ghum* after his father rejects his relationship with Kajol. Being the jerk that I am, I even came up with this plan where Vedika would tell Micky how much she likes him, and once he reciprocates she would laugh and say, "In your face!". She never did it for obvious reasons.

We had been dating for 4-5 months now, and nothing had happened physically. I wanted to make the first move but was afraid to do so, and she being the "Indian woman" didn't think it was right for her to make the first move. I suppose we never found time alone either. Towards the final few months of our school days, we both were really engrossed in studies, as 10th standard board exams determined which junior college (11th & 12th grade) you went to. Both of us wanted to go to a good college being good students. My board exams had some drama associated with it too. Right before our algebra exam, the examination center I was in caught fire due to some electrical short circuit. This caused a delay in our exam, and all the students were frantically calling their parents up to tell them about the incident, and to inform them that they will be late getting home. The guy in front of me in the line at a booth called his mom and said, "*Maa idhar aag lagi hui hai*" (Mom, there is a fire here). His mom misunderstood that statement and thought the movie Fire, which had just released and was about lesbians in India, was playing close to the exam center. Her reply was, "*Beta, picture mat dekh. Exam pe dhyan de*" (Son, don't watch the movie now, focus on your exams). It was hard to write my algebra exam after that with a straight face. After every problem I solved, I would keep replaying the conversation the kid had with his mother and I would crack up. One of the supervisors even warned me that if I didn't stop giggling, she would throw me out of the exam. During my geography exams, I did not know the answers to match the column questions. Since my going to a good college depended on it, I had to get those answers somehow. There was a girl sitting right next to me in the adjacent row, who used to write a lot in every exam. So I thought she would know the answers. I decided to ask her the answers, and she was more than happy in helping me out. I stepped outside after the exam and compared answers with a friend of mine, an intelligent friend, and the entire match the column answers were wrong. That was the day I decided never to trust women ever again.

I got through the rest of the exams without any further incidents. I spent the vacations practicing badminton, playing a lot of badminton tournaments, including playing the state championships, where I lost miserably, and my doubles partner and I were taken to the limit by a couple of U-13 boys in the first round, and the top seeds ran all over us in the second round. Vedika, in the meanwhile, was busy focusing on roller skating and trying to learn table tennis. We had a good summer overall, spent a lot of time together without any physical contact. The results of the board exams were out soon. Vedika got 85%, while I got 81%. Though I was not satisfied with my result, it was the end of my days at GHK high school. No matter how much I make fun of this school, I had a wonderful time with all my teachers and friends in one way or the other. I would like to thank the school for helping me where I am right now, jobless.

Anecdote : The budding poet

In school, when you learn something new, you always want to implement that somehow and impress everyone in class. The day we were taught rhyming words was the day I decided to write a poem, which if I may add was read out aloud in class by our English teacher.

Mother mother you are so kind
Whatever you wear, I don't mind
You tell me that birds have feathers
But you don't tell that to my brother

When you come home you make me study
And sometimes you make me worry
When I study and you start the mixer
I feel like I am being hit by a boxer

24 Hours you take care of our health
As you know, we are your wealth

Yeah, I definitely was the next Edgar Allan Poe in the making.

Lose yourself

Personally, I didn't know a single kid, from GHK or any other high school, who were not eager to get into junior college, including me. This new chapter in our lives provided a lot of opportunities; no more compulsion to attend all lectures, no uniforms to worry about, lots of new women and to learn how to earn some money to spend on these women, by hook or by crook. Of course the women weren't my concern as I was in a relationship with Vedika. We all know how first relationships can be; everything feels good, you are smiling all the time, even if you are not happy you make yourself believe you are happy because you are obviously going to get married and have a couple of kids.

As she had a better percentage in the 10th std exams, she got into Mithibai College, one of the reputed junior colleges in the city, while I missed out on it and had to settle for National College. Now National College was apparently a hot spot for wannabes. According to me, every junior college was a hot spot for the so-called wannabes. Everyone wants to be cool. The cool crowd from school wants to continue being cool, the hot girls still want to get noticed, the crowd that was neglected in school gets a new start in life, we were all starting from square one and it was tough to be accepted. Some colored their hair to get noticed, some wore agonizingly low cut jeans without bothering to shave back there, guys would sit on bikes outside the gate of the college and rev their engines all day, "curvy" women would wear tight tops to show off their well endowed bosoms which inadvertently also showed off their belly fat. You name it and kids did it to get noticed. What did I do? I dressed like a bum. I didn't do it consciously I suppose but I would end up wearing t-shirts with all possible colors that would stretch up to my knees along with baggy jeans. I really wish I had a picture to show you how ridiculous I looked. It was in no way an attempt to be cool, but I think it was an attempt to stay away from any sort of trouble and go under the radar.

First day of college is always a bit scary. You hear rumors about seniors ragging juniors by making them beg, or making them pay for their bills in restaurants. I was a bit afraid too. Considering I dressed like a bum anyway, I could very well be forced to beg which in turn might yield a lot of money based on my appearance, or I could be asked to pay for bills which I had no money for. Every day my mom would give me about Rs.30 as allowance, which was not bad I guess but was not the best either. As I was over 6 feet tall, I got hold of another friend from GHK who was just as tall and walked into the college hoping that two big guys would not be bothered, and I was right. We made it safely to class but the rest of the day was spent introducing ourselves in every lecture, standing up, and saying something "fun" about ourselves. I really wished I was ragged than go through that.

My class was the one that had taken French as the second language. This meant a lot of snobs from good high schools. I particularly remember this one guy called Murtaza who warned me that if I ever took his name out loud in class again, I should watch my back. That is what junior college was all about, empty threats. Every guy tries to act all macho but no one wants to get into fights or any sort of trouble. I would notice people yelling at each other all day and daring the other person to go ahead and touch them, with the other guy reciprocating in the same manner. I would have given my daily allowance to see an actual fight but unfortunately I never witnessed one.

French division also meant many good-looking women for some reason. Some of them we just ogled at like Rachna Patel, while some of the cute ones actually spoke to us. I assure you I would somehow make sure that the girl knew I had a girlfriend in the first conversation we had itself. It was like I had to clear my conscience. I had a couple of really close friends, girls. One was Priya, who claimed to be cousins with actress Rani Mukherjee. I believed her because if you had to lie about knowing a celebrity, Rani Mukherjee would be the last person you would associate yourself with. Priya and I were good friends, and she would share her love life with me. She was dating a 25yr old guy at that time, we were 16 then. Either the guy really liked her, or he was a pervert who had never heard of statutory rape. Either way it was creepy. She would even delve into some details of their physical relationship too, like the time when they tried to kiss but his braces got caught in her lips and started bleeding. Some details are best never told. Then there was Prish. I call her Prish because this girl was apparently so madly in love with me that she created an email ID by meshing her name with mine and called it Prish. Unfortunately, I did not know about this email ID until a very long time so I was still good friends with her. Then there was Sherri. Sherri wasn't what anyone would call good looking but I thought she had a hot body. I always had a thing for petite girls, and she was petite alright. And if that wasn't enough, she would wear these tank tops and skirts which really got me going. You have to understand my friends that for a guy who had been in a relationship for over 7 months and not even kissed his girlfriend, all this was too much to handle. Thankfully, National College had a badminton court where I would take out all my pent up sexual frustration pretty much all day. I never attended any lectures, and would be on the badminton court. This resulted in the vice-principal calling my parents, along with the parents of many other kids if I may add, to come meet him because of my lack of attendance. Unfortunately, my mother knew the vice-principal, as she herself was the vice-principal of the college where she taught. She was embarrassed to come but still decided to anyway. She spoke to the vice-principal and they were sitting in their office. A peon was asked to get me from class to the vice-principal's office. Of course, I was not found in class, as I had not attended any lecture that day either. You can only imagine how long I was grounded for after that.

Being in different colleges did not keep Vedika and me from meeting. The colleges were not too far away from each other so either she would come to National or I would go over to her college. One day she came to my apartment complex, and we were sitting on the steps of a building which was nowhere close to mine. We spoke for a while, which we always did, but that day for some reason we were sitting really close to each other. Maybe it was my desperation, or maybe it was just a coincidence. Either way, I was happy that we were that close. After a few minutes of talking, I decided to make my move. I just leaned in and kissed her. And as soon as I did, my friend's mother who lived in that particular building walked in.

My first reaction was to push Vedika away as if she was forcing herself on me. Then I smiled and exchanged pleasantries with my friend's mother. After she left, I had to convince Vedika to come close to me again and eventually we did kiss again. Things started moving faster from that day onwards. We had to make up for lost time. Every time we met, we would take it a step forward. However, we were very careful not to go all the way. It was just that we had too many myths in our heads about the sacred ritual, and also it was a big step which we wanted to take our time with. A few days before my 16th birthday, I was at her place and we were watching a movie. After the movie, we sat on her bed just talking about random things. I was about to leave and kissed her goodbye. However, this particular kiss goodbye was a bit too long and passionate. In the words of Sir Etienne Garrard, a gentleman can hint at a lot of things but never say it out loud. So all I have to say my friends is that that was the day I became a man.

Physical relationships are important but they should never take over a relationship. I have, and will always maintain that the physical closeness is more important than mental compatibility. However, in our case, it had just taken over our relationship. Kids always think that intercourse is the best thing in life. It might be good or bad depending on people, but it is definitely not something that would keep a relationship going just on those bases. For all those guys who believe sex is the ultimate pleasure, try sports. Football did it for me. I honestly believe football is better than sex. This might seem like a bold statement to make but I have really thought about this a lot, and football is just more satisfying. Please don't misunderstand me, sex is good. I might even call it a basic necessity because due to pent up sexual tension, many people get frustrated. However, there is a lot of tension associated with sex too. Women might have things going through their mind during the act like, "Do I give good head?", "Am I good enough to satisfy him?", "Do I look good naked?", "Are my breasts big enough?", and of course "Great, I will have to fake it again". For men, while doing it, the thoughts are more on the lines of, "Am I big enough?", "I wonder what really turns her on?", "I hope she is not faking it", "God, her friend looked hot today", and "Aaah Megan Fox!" For an activity that is supposed to give you pleasure, there is too much anticipation and anxiety attached to it. The thought of having sex, and actually going through the process could give you a lot of stress. In the end, though you might be satisfied, was it really worth all that? Come football and you don't have to worry about anything. Some might argue that you might wonder about your performance. Maybe, but that is at a more professional level. When you play at a recreational level, it is more about going out there and having fun and running around like you are 10 years old again. You do not care about anything while playing football; your mind is just focused on playing the game. And the feeling you get when you score as a striker/mid-fielder, execute a perfect sliding tackle as a defender, or make a spectacular save as a goalkeeper is nothing short of an orgasmic one.

Unfortunately for Vedika and me, we focused too much on the physical aspects of our relationship. It reached a point where we had stopped talking to each other even while sitting at her place. Slowly but surely our relationship was falling apart. We did not even realize what was happening till it reached a point where we thought we were just not compatible any more. One fine day, we spoke about it at length; about how we should share our feelings more with each other and not just satisfy our physical needs. We even decided to take our physical intimacy back to square one so that we could work things out. And surprisingly, it turned out to be a great idea. We would continue meeting at her place every day, but this time around we spoke a lot more and things were going great once again.

But all good runs have to come to an end. We were bound to be caught one time or the other, or at least come close to it. It was voting day (something I didn't know for some reason), and I decided to go over to her place as usual. We did our usual routine, and I was about to leave when she just looked out of the window, only to find her dad's car back in the lot. She screamed at me to get out of the house asap. Right then we heard a knock on the door, she looked through the peephole and it was her dad. I was stuck in her house! Her room had a bathroom, which I was rushed into immediately. I was standing there with my shoes in my hand, pretty much pissing in my pants. The trouble was that her little brother would have come back from school in half-an-hour or so, and if that happened there was no way I would have gotten out alive. It seemed like an eternity had passed when she knocked on the door and asked me to run out as quickly as possible because her father had gone into the common bathroom. If someone had timed my run that day out of her apartment, I am sure I would give Usain Bolt a run for his money. Her building, her apartment complex, and even the road she lived on for that matter were only a blur to me. I ran on my naked feet till I felt my lungs might burst. When I called her the next day, for the first 5-10 minutes we could not do anything but just laugh. You would think an experience like that would teach us a lesson but no, we were on a mission. On Valentine's Day, neither of us had to go to college, so I told my mom I had chemistry practicals and went straight to her place. My friend Narayan, one of the most intelligent people I have met in my life, calls up at my place asking for me. My mom informed him that I was in college attending practicals, to which he casually replies, "But practicals were canceled today". Right after he said it he realized he was more stupid than J. Howard Marshall II for marrying Anna Nicole Smith. Somehow, he managed to get Vedika's home phone number through a few connections (I did not have a cell phone till my undergrad years) and warn me about the impending danger at home. I gave him an earful and headed home quickly, with the first words coming out of my mouth as soon as I got home being, "Stupid practicals got canceled". You would think a mother would believe her child when he genuinely lies to her, but not my mother. She checked my wallet, checked the Rs.30 she had given me that morning, out of which I had spent 20 already on rickshaw fare to and fro. When asked how I managed to spend Rs.20 within an hour's time, I replied without a pause that I used it for rickshaw and to buy a soda. Satisfied, my mom left for work. For all the young people reading this, do not lie to your parents. But if you do lie, make sure you are lying for a very good cause. Lying for a good cause makes it a white lie.

To continue with my narrow escapes, I was alone one day at my place and Vedika decided to come over. We were in the middle of fooling around, when I heard some sort of noise in the house. It was a very soft sound, more like a click. Usually when I heard such sounds, I ignored it but I decided to check it out that day, and man was I glad I did. I walked out of my room and saw my mom taking off her sandals in complete stealth mode. Sometimes I really wonder if she has been trained to be a ninja or a marine. Maybe she was really Snake Eyes. She moved ever so silently. To warn Vedika somehow, I started talking to my mom in Malayalam. The smart kid that she was, Vedika quickly got up and sat on the desktop in my room. I went back into the room and pretended to be showing Vedika how to do something on the Internet, which was ironic considering she would teach me everything including making my first email id. My mom saw her, said hi and went into my parent's room to change. After five minutes, Vedika left and my mom immediately asked me, "So was that Vedika? The girl you talk to on the phone pretty much every day?" When I replied in the affirmative, her response was, "She is ugly".

Apart from all these close encounters of a dangerous kind, we actually went out a lot too, though most of our dates would be at McDonald's. But I also made an effort to meet her college friends, and would try to put on my best behavior in front of them. Everyone knows that it is imperative that your girlfriend's friends like you. And I did my best. And a couple of them did think I was nice, particularly Vanita. Vedika had some interesting friends too. There was a guy Ganesh who took it upon himself to instill Indian values in Vedika. If he ever saw us standing close, or me having an arm around her, or us dancing close, he would tell her how she should not do it because I might get turned on and turn into a rapist. There was a couple, Ankush and Kareena, in that group who just could not stop making out. I have nothing against PDA(Public display of affection), I enjoy it myself at times, but there is a limit to what you should be doing in public, and sticking your tongue down your partner's throat in definitely out of the limit. And honestly, when not-so-good-looking people do it, it is a bit more disgusting. Again, all of you might think I am just being shallow here, but I am sure you all feel the same way. But here is where it got really interesting. Sometime later, Ankush confessed to Kareena that he was gay. He even liked some guy. When I think about it, making out with that girl would have turned anyone gay. She had a mustache that gave me a complex. Then again maybe it was the mustache that attracted him towards her, though to his disappointment he later found out she didn't actually have what he was looking for. Though I was never the kind of person to hang out with Vedika's friends all the time, after this particular revelation, I definitely tried to keep my distance to avoid any further surprises.

As I mentioned earlier, I really got into badminton after my 10th std exams. I wasn't really a very good player, but a decent player. I never thought a sport like badminton would make me popular in college but it did. National college had many intra-college events. College was split into five teams and each team was given points based on their performance in each event. Badminton of course was my specialty. In my first year, I pretty much decimated all opposition. You can imagine the crazy amount of attention I got. I even had an extremely cute girl come up and ask me how I played so well. Of course, at that time I was too young, hence stupid, to realize that she was kind of infatuated by me and that I should play it cool and flirt a bit. Instead, I sat her down and gave her a nice hour-long lecture on how to play badminton. I have never seen a woman walk away as fast as she did that day*.

By the end of the first year of college, I had a big fan following, I was being accosted by people I had never seen before but who doesn't mind the attention. Come second year, and the guy I used to play doubles with in tournaments and practiced together, Sachin, joined National College. Sachin was a very good player. As a matter of fact, we won most of our doubles matches because he was so good. And because we played with each other so much, we both knew each other's game very well. We won matches after matches and in no time were going to state!

Representing Mumbai was a big thing for us. The state inter-college events were held in Aurangabad. The evening we had to leave, four of us teammates, met up at the train station, on the platform Mr. Bharve had asked us to meet. We got there, along with Sachin's father, and were waiting for our team manager. Mr. Bharve comes in pretty much on schedule and says, "Lets go buy tickets". Our jaws dropped. There was a better chance of me running into Cindy Crawford right at that moment on the platform than us getting reservations an hour before the train left. Sachin's father was furious, and in his infuriated state he gave Mr. Bharve an earful. I had never heard a parent curse someone so much in front of kids, but it was hilarious. So we hopped on the train without tickets hoping that there would be no ticket collectors that night on the train.

*Ipshita if you are reading this, call me!

According to Murphy's Law, *anything that can go wrong will go wrong*, and it did for us too; we met the ticket collector. The sweet talking kids that we were, we convinced the guy that we were representing Mumbai, and that he had to allow us to sit anywhere we could so that we could make to the state tournament. He eventually did allow us to travel, however, he told us not to sit on any of the seats as they were reserved. And what was our dear team manager doing all the while we were convincing the TC? He was sound asleep and snoring so loud that it was hard for us to have a conversation with the TC. For the rest of the almost 7 hour journey, we sat right next to the stinky toilets. The Mumbai collegiate badminton team ladies and gentlemen.

We reached Aurangabad late in the night. We were all really tired as none of us could get any sleep on the train, thanks to the smell of ammonia. I have to tell you, if you are exposed to the odor of ammonia long enough, it doesn't feel that bad any more. After 7 hours, it would smell as good as Hugo Boss or Issey Miyake. We were to stay at the state's accommodation for athletes. After reaching the place well past midnight, we were glad to find a mattress a piece for all of us. No one even bothered to change, and we all had a good night's sleep. The matches were to begin in the afternoon so we did not have to get up early. After a nice long sleep, I got up and looked out of the window. It was a beautiful view overlooking some mountains with sunlight bouncing off the dew on the leaves of the trees. I was finally happy with something Mr. Bharve had done. Right at that moment, Sachin came running into the room. His face was white, as if he had seen a ghost. Catching his breath, he asked me to go take a look in the bathroom. Now the bathroom was common for the whole building apparently. I was half expecting a dead body in there. I stepped in to find four doors on the left side and four doors on the right. The doors on the left turned out to be showers. So the four doors on the right had to be toilets. Then I opened the first toilet door only to realize why my doubles partner was so horrified. The Indian style toilet had a small pile of excreta sitting right in the middle. I almost barfed but shut the door quickly. Opened the second door and it was the same story, just that the pile was a bit bigger. As I continued opening all the doors, the size of the pile kept increasing. It was like being stuck in a nightmare. All of us had to take a dump, so we decided to clean the toilet with the smallest pile with water. After it was done, I was the first one to use the toilet. Though still disgusted, I somehow managed to sit down. Suddenly, I felt like I was being watched for some reason, or that I was sitting in an open field*. I looked back, something very hard to do while sitting on an Indian toilet, and see this huge window behind me which has no windows. With all the shit (literally) going on, we had failed to notice the huge open window in that booth. If there were anyone standing on the roof of the adjoining building, I would actually be mooning them without any intention of doing it. And to top it all off, I saw a giant spider right over the tap. It was the worst start to the day ever. After the toilet incident, none of us wanted to eat at the cafeteria in that place, though Mr. Bharve was very keen on doing that and saving some money.

We decided it would be better to go have lunch at a restaurant. Though we did not expect the best service in that

*One of our teammates, Joel, decided to take a dump in an open field itself. He could not get himself to go in that toilet.

remote neighborhood, waiting for an hour to get our food was a bit of a stretch. However, that was the only decent restaurant we could find so it became the only place we ate from for the couple of days we were there. Of course there isn't much to talk about the actual reason we were there. In our first round itself, we played a college which had two of the state's top seeds, Nishad Dravid and Soham Gadgil. I think we had a good day to get a few points off them at least. After our loss, we were informed that Sachin and I were selected to play the singles draw from which a few players would be selected for a national badminton camp. They had to pick two players from each college and that was the only reason why we were asked. If they were to select players based on performance, I believe we would have been advised never to play badminton again, apart from in our backyards. On that trip, we also got quite friendly with the college team representing Mumbai in the women's section, Ruia College. They did not have a great trip either and wanted to leave that night itself, and not wait for the singles events which was the next day. We had the same opinion, but Mr. Bharve said we should play. So at night when he was sound asleep, the four of us sneaked out and caught a bus back to Mumbai along with the girls from Ruia. The journey back was much more comfortable, though we didn't get much sleep again as all of us were up talking for most of the way back. After a couple of days, the badminton team was called into the principal's office, where Mr. Bharve was already present. The principal asked us why we had left without playing the singles event. We were honest and told her that it was a lost cause to play against the top players in the state. She in turn gave us a big speech on how that is not the right attitude for a sportsman, and that we would never know unless we tried. It was like telling me to go up against Mike Tyson for a round of boxing to find out if I could win. I don't have to get into the ring with Iron Mike to know I will get the crap beat out of me.

All this while, my relationship with Vedika was deteriorating. Both of us had new friends, new lives which we had to give time to. Sometimes she would be jealous, while sometimes it would be me. She was quite jealous of Priya as Priya was a very cute girl after all. All you men out there never tell a girl that your girlfriend is jealous of them, and then go and tell your girlfriend that you told the other girl that. No good comes out of it, I say that with experience. We got into a lot of fights because of Prish too because Vedika thought that Prish falling in love with me had a lot to do with me flirting with her. I do admit I had a tendency to flirt with women, and I still do. It is not a bad thing. Everyone has urges as human beings, to interact with new people, to make others like them, and to impress the ones you find attractive. According to me, flirting with a woman is fine as long as you don't follow up on it. Subtle flirting will not harm anyone, but you have to know your limits of course, and I knew mine. But when it came to Prish, I still maintain that I never flirted with her. We were good friends and I treated her like one of the guys more than anything else. However, Vedika thought otherwise.

One thing about having fights when you are in an immature relationship as a teenager is that every fight meant that you broke up. And after everything is sorted out, you are back together again. It is like The Undertaker dying in the WWE. He has died so many times, and of course has resurrected every single time. I mean the guy did it more times than Jesus for crying out loud. My friends got so tired of me telling them that I had broken up and then a few days later that I was back with Vedika, that they asked me to keep my private life private only.

Towards the end of second year in junior college, 12th std, both of us were really focusing on our board exams. Forget meeting, we barely even spoke on the phone. These board exams are really important because they determine if you can get into a good engineering college or not. To make sure I got all the help I needed, my mother through all the connections she had amongst professors would find out who the external examiner was in each of my three practicals, physics, chemistry, and biology, and make sure the external knew that a vice-principal's son was going to give his examination, and would somehow ensure they even had my seat number. If not the external, the internal examiner was notified. During my physics practicals, while I was conducting experiments, my mom was actually sitting in the examination hall with the external examiner. Talk about knowing your grades even before giving your exam. After my final written exam, I met Vedika outside my college, we went to Star City theater to watch a movie, well mostly to just take out all the frustration pent up in us from the exams and the months of studying. I felt bad for the family that was sitting behind us with little kids.

You see my mother always wanted a doctor and an engineer in the house. My brother, three years elder to me, is a brilliant chap and he actually had the option to pick between medicine and engineering and he had chosen engineering. The day he did that, I consoled my mom by saying I would become a doctor, though I had no interest in it. We had a separate medical entrance examination for which my folks put me in coaching classes. I was least interested and would end up just going there to meet some friends. But at the same time, I also met some girls I developed a liking for. I am very bad at breaking up, as a matter of fact, I just can't do it. As a result, when I am not into the relationship any more, I tend to flirt around a lot, way more than what I would usually do so that my partner would get frustrated and would end things with me. And this is exactly what happened. Vedika realized what I was up to and we met up one day at McDonald's. I knew what was coming, I wanted it too. But it still hurt. I knew this was not just another stupid breakup. I knew it was the real deal. We caught a rickshaw together to go home as I could drop her on the way. Tears kept pouring out of my eyes no matter how much I tried to control it. You have to understand that she had just ended my first ever relationship, which had lasted for almost three long years, it had to be painful. I dropped her off and we said our goodbyes. We promised to talk to each other always, and to always be friends, like you always do at the end of a painful breakup. Not the best of ideas considering it only makes it harder for you to get over the person. Usually, you lose contact sooner or later, or eventually faze the person out of your life. I am very happy to say that Vedika and me still talk pretty often and are still good friends.

After my breakup, and before my engineering days started, I had a lot of flings. And I mean a lot. I am not trying to tell you that I was good with girls or that I am good looking, or trying to boast about the fact that I was with many women. It just happened somehow. After a long relationship, there is most definitely going to be a rebound, and I had mine too with a girl named Neha. Though we were officially dating for eight months, out of those eight months, I was in Kerala for a good three months while she was in Gujarat for almost two or three months. In the time we actually spent together, we were always with friends and never alone. A peck on the cheeks was the high point of my physical relationship with this girl. And the whole time, I had a big crush on her friend too, and a genuine crush. Again, it was Neha who ended things with me. But after that, I really concentrated on her friend. We spent a lot of time together, went for movies, went for lunch, hold hands, and kiss on the cheeks. I had more physical contact with her than I did with Neha whom I was dating. When I felt that she was ready to be asked out, I told her how I felt, and she told me that she considered me only as a friend. I wish I could tell everyone her name because she was the closest thing to friends with benefits, if not the actual thing. How can you give all possible hints to a guy and then just be friends?

After that, I decided it was futile to look for a meaningful relationship, and decided to play the field. And play the field I did. In that period of time, I met some of the weirdest women. A girl who kept giving me missed calls, not because her prepaid card was low on balance or something, but because she missed me! I just completely ignored her after that explanation. Then there was a girl who stayed close to my colony, and looked good whenever I saw her from a distance, if I ignored her weird gait. I knew she was a junior from GHK, and managed to get her number. I asked her out on a date, and the first thing I noticed was that she doesn't wax. I just could not handle it after a couple of dates. I always had a few drinks before I went on a date with her to blur out the hairy image. I took her to my favorite theater Star City again, but while kissing her all I could think of was that her upper lip hair coming in contact with my lips. So soon I started ignoring her too*. I met girls at concerts, theaters, coffee shops, and would end up going out on dates with them. I even dated a girl from my colony who was five years elder to me. It was a perfect life then, and many of my friends were jealous of me too. But soon my engineering life started, and things changed. Don't know if the changes were for good or bad, but they definitely changed.

---

*I know it is a complete douchebag move to just ignore someone like that but I'm just not good at ending things.

Anecdote : Myth busters

My brother has helped me a lot throughout my life. He has always been there for me. He is even providing me food and shelter while I am writing this book. But as a kid, he told me a lot of things just to fool me, which I believed for a very long time.

Myth 1: I was very scared of horror movies or horror shows. Actually, I still am. Every night after watching something that involved ghosts, my brother would tell me that I should sleep before 12am because between 12am and 4am, all the ghosts come out. I would always be terrified of getting up between that four hour time slot. My class went for a school trip to Lonavala when I was in 9th grade, and we were all playing dark room. After a couple of hours, I looked at the clock and realized it was almost midnight. I quickly got under the sheets and told everyone that we should sleep because ghosts come out after midnight. There was a moment of silence followed by hysterical laughter. I never heard the end of that one for the last two years of my GHK days.

Myth 2: I got into the same college my brother was in for engineering. While he was in his final year, I was in my first. We went to college together early morning and would come back whenever we could in the evening. Considering the heat and humidity in India, we could switch on the air conditioning in the car most of the times. However, my brother always kept the fan speed one level lower than maximum. When asked why he doesn't keep it on full, he gave me a long explanation on why maximum speed would not give the best circulation, and that this was the perfect speed for ideal cooling. One day when I had the car, I decided to drop off a couple of friends to the nearby train station, and I kept the fan speed on what my brother used to keep it at. My friends asked me why I was not turning it to maximum as they were sweating and I gave them my brother's explanation. There was again silence followed by laughter.

Myth 3: My brother once told me that if you pour water into alcohol and keep it for a while, the water ferments into alcohol. I had some of my friends over one day after a football game and we decided to have a few drinks. The broke students we were, we decided to make a couple of drinks from my dad's, then full, bottle of rum. A couple turned to a few and before we knew it the bottle barely had anything left. I had to act quickly. I filled it up with water to the brink, hoping it would ferment by night when my dad got home. At night when I got back home after playtime, my father asked me if I had anyone over. I said I had a couple of friends over and also inquired why he was asking. He showed me the bottle of rum and said, "This was dark when I left and tasted like rum. Now I can see through the bottle and it tastes like water". So much for fermentation.

Me? An Engineer Part 1

As I mentioned earlier, I got into the same engineering college as my brother, Dwarkadas J. Sanghvi College of Engineering (DJSCOE/DJ). DJSCOE was a very reputed college for engineering and I was excited to start, though being a Production Engineering student is a tough job. First few days in college were boring with the same old routine of running away from seniors to avoid being ragged. I have never understood the whole culture of ragging. How does making juniors do something embarrassing help them get well acquainted with the seniors? If you want to know me better, just accost me and I will give you my life history if required. But I suppose traditions are like voting in Bihar. You know your vote doesn't matter because the elections are fixed, but you do it anyway as it is your right. The only good part about the first few days of engineering was that Vanita, Vedika's friend, was in the same class so I at least knew one person in the class. Though she tried her level best to avoid me, I would talk to her at every opportunity, not because she was attractive, but because I did not want to come off as someone who was a loner and knew nobody in class. But after the first few days of trials and tribulations, I finally started enjoying myself. I found out that the varsity football team was holding selections and I tried out for the team, and to my surprise I made it as well. Now I had seniors, final year students, who knew me. This was very exciting. I would hang out with them a lot in between lectures, during lectures, whenever. Of course, while trying to act cool you tend to make major blunders. We were once sitting outside the college when one of the girls from my class walked past us, and all my teammates were just staring at her and saying out loud how good she looked. Now I had to play this cool and make it seem like that extremely cute girl wasn't cute enough for me. So I said, "Come on guys. She is strictly ok. She has got such a big dick!" Yes I said dick. I wanted to say ass but for some reason my brain wasn't in collaboration with my mouth that day. From that day on, I was known as 'Big Dick', and not in a good way.

There were three things that I had decided I would never do. First, I would never have alcoholic drinks outside my house. My reasoning behind this was my folks would give me a couple of drinks anyway at home so why bother get drunk at an unknown place? Second, I would never go to a nightclub. I had seen too many movies where the crowd in clubs were just drunk and had no inhibitions. Even the ambience was never too appealing for me. Last but not the least; I decided never to do drugs, for obvious reasons. During my football tryouts, I met Baggy. Baggy was another guy who was trying out for the team, and he was for some reason selected too though he sucked more than Lewinsky on Clinton. But he was a second year production engineering student, which made him my go-to guy for everything. We became good friends and one day he invited me for a beer at a bar near the college. From that day on, almost every other day we would have two big bottles of beer along with lunch and then proceeded to attend the remaining lectures. Any function meant coming for it drunk too. Each department in the college had separate events, and the college on a whole had a big event called *Parichay* (Introduction). Now these festivals as they were called had numerous activities or sub-events. And it was the same lineup for every festival. There would be a robotics competition where students from different colleges would build "robots" and try to win the competition. Most of these robots would just be cars run with the help of motors. How cool. Then there would be random events like Pictionary or rink football. Rink football had crazy rules too with each team having four players, and one player has to be a girl. I am not saying girls cannot play football. I have seen some amazing female football players here in the US. But Indian women should not play football. I formed a team for one of these football events and recruited Vanita to be the girl in our team. All the teams put the girl in the small goal, and we did the same. Considering the goals were small, the goalie was not allowed to use their hands. However, Vanita completely forgot this and caught the ball with her hands resulting in a penalty. Now I can understand someone doing it once, but how insanely stupid do you have to be to catch the ball again with your hands? If it was not allowed the first time around, I am guessing it will not be allowed the second time either!

Parichay was on a much bigger scale than the small individual festivals. There were singing competitions and band competitions. Most of the bands were great and a real treat to listen to. One event that was always on the lineup for every festival in every college was a fashion show. I never ever understood the concept of a fashion show in any college. The clothes were not designer clothes. Best-case scenario, the clothes would be from some local third grade store, but most of the time the clothes would be from the personal wardrobes of the so-called models. I can assure you not a single person in the crowd must be looking at the clothes each model adorns and be thinking, "That outfit is good, I should buy it". All the guys in the crowd are looking the female models and taking mental pictures to go home and satisfy themselves. Some guys even look at the male models and admire their physique. Girls in the crowd just keep bitching about how ugly some girl on the ramp looked, or how they could see a particular models baby fat. It is wonderful to hear these conversations in the crowd when you are absolutely hammered, and that was an absolute prerequisite before attending any event.

Some fashion shows had more dancing than walking. I particularly remember this one college who had their male models do around 50 pushups on stage. How is that a fashion show?

A mutual friend of Narayan and me was from that college, and upon seeing this 50 pushup feet, was amazed and could not stop talking about how cool it was. I did not know if I should doubt the poor guy's intelligence, or if I should blame the society for making the lamest things the coolest things ever. Case in point: Ugg boots.

I suppose it was a big deal to be in the fashion show. It meant you were one of the better-looking people in your college, a rare commodity especially when it comes to engineering colleges. Unfortunately, these "models" thought being in a lame college fashion show meant they were the hottest property around. I would not blame them for that; I blame all the others who give them that social status of being very hot property. These mediocre looking guys and girls were made to believe that they were no less than Tyson Beckford or Josie Maran. If you think I am one of those sore losers who is just bitching about the show because I could not make it, then you are mistaken. I was actually asked to participate in it a couple of times, to my astonishment, but I humbly refused. It was not that I did not want to be around the hot women, it was just that I could not do it in my senses, and a drunk model isn't always fun.

There are some things Indians should never do. These include playing American football, making Indian porn, talking in an American accent in spite of never having been to the USA, making reality shows, and covering a legendary metal band. For *Parichay*, we had a band called Brahma perform as the main event. Brahma was known for their Metallica covers, and had a standard lineup of songs which included, For Whom the Bell Tolls, Enter Sandman etc. However, that day they had come up with a few new covers, one of them being Battery. When James Hetfield sings Battery, with his amazing voice and a deep tone, he sings "Bat-uh-ray!" The Brahma lead singer had the voice of a 16-year-old boy whose voice had not yet cracked, and he yelled at the top of his voice, "Batter-eee! Batter-eee!" Though I have to admit some of the Indian bands are really good, and a pleasure to listen to. Parikrama, Pin Drop Violence, Moist Vaginas, Zero, and the new and upcoming band SummerPint Junkie, to name a few, are good. Unfortunately, bands like Brahma spoil it for everyone.

After all the fun and games, there was something else we had to do too. I think it was called studying. Engineering in India was a big joke, and still might be. The last month was the only time when people opened their books to study in a four-month semester. I am talking about normal human beings when I say people, not the geeks or the nerds. Mid-terms were just a formality. With the mid-terms only accounting for 10% of the final grades, most people chose to not study and walk out of the examination hall as soon as possible. In fact, I personally have at times kept bets with my friends as to who would walk out first; and I can proudly say I always won. Then came the final exams, the ones I was not at all prepared for. I realized how big a mistake it was to not study a single word for the mid-terms. There were 6 subjects and the syllabi were huge. There was no way in hell I would have finished everything. This is when I learned the most magical word in any engineer's life; option. Every student, apart from the toppers, would leave a few chapters as optional chapters which meant that in previous papers of the same subject, those particular chapters either accounted for very few points, or no points whatsoever. These chapters were only to be learned if students had enough time to go through the rest of the important stuff thoroughly. Unfortunately for my first semester exam, and for all the remaining exams in my engineering life, my optional chapters in every subject were more than 60% of the syllabus. The good thing about Mumbai University was there was an Allowed To Keep Terms (ATKT) system which meant that students who failed in subjects were allowed to go through to the next term, and just had to give those papers again. My first semester results revealed I failed in 2 subjects. This was the first time in my life I had ever failed, and it sucked. Though there was nothing I should have been complaining about. What else could I have expected with my schedule for the entire semester being football practice in the morning, Kingfisher strong in the afternoon for lunch and football/badminton/cricket in the evening in my colony? I really took it to my heart to change my ways in the next semester.

Procrastination is a bitch. I kept delaying the day when I would open my books and start studying. In the end, there was the one-month study leave left and I was screwed again. During these study leaves, most of the students would come to college to study as most of the classrooms were kept open, and so was the library. Studying in college also meant that if you had any doubt, there would be someone from your class around from whom you could clear your doubt. I never liked studying in college. I liked being alone, and being in my room to study. I have a bad habit of lying down on my bed to read. It would mean falling asleep a lot of times reading boring subjects, but it was just what I was comfortable with. But I also used to go to college at times if some friend of mine agreed to teach me a chapter or two in a particular subject. During these study leaves, the college was filled with students. Even the hallways were lined with students studying. Many of the guys would not shave during this period citing lack of time to shave. I would understand a woman not waxing due to lack of time, but how much time does it take to shave any way? I could make out that some of them didn't take a shower for days too from the odor emanating from them. I still believe all this was just pretense to show people how hard you had been studying. I was one of the very few people there who would look spic-and-span. Then again, the dirty ones passed exams with flying colors while I flunked the first time around. Maybe I should have gone with the dirty look. After the second semester exams, I was pretty nervous about the results. I had taken 8 exams, 6 of the second semester and 2 from the previous one in which I had failed. First year exams were university level exams, and because of that, the final first year results were put up in the university. In the university, they would just put up your seat number which proved that you had indeed passed the year. Missing number meant you had failed. I frantically searched for my number but could not find it anywhere. Finally, at the bottom of the page of the Pass Class list, I saw it, my number. I circled it and wrote, "Anish Rulz". I do not know why I used the 'Z" but I guess it was the cool thing to write at that point of time in my life.

First year of engineering, all the departments had common subjects. So production engineering students were spread out over different divisions. Come second year, and we were all put together in one class. It was a bit of a disadvantage for us as all the other departments were with their classmates for one full year already while we now had to spend time to get to know one another. It was like the first year of college all over again. Though I barely ever attended classes, the little time I got to spend in my class was enough for me to make a judgment about my new classmates. There was the class topper Amit Jariwala*, then there were the minions, including me. Compared to Amit, all of us were minions when it came to academics. There were only 3 girls in the whole class. However, the class did have some very peculiar characters when it came to the guys. There were Rohan and Karan who could not stop sucking up to professors 24/7. There was Kartik who was so nice that he would complete others' assignments first before his own. There was Chintan because, well every class needed a fat kid. Shreyas, who wanted to make fun of everyone, but if

*Amit went on to be the Mumbai University topper in production engineering in the final year. Kudos to him.

made fun of would burst into tears. Aniruddha Mehta was the most loud and obnoxious guy in the whole of DJSCOE whom everyone avoided, or at least tried their best to avoid. Vinayak, Bhavesh and Kamlesh who had only one thing one their mind; to eye rape every girl. There was Bhavin who I think was around 40 years old when he joined us in the second year, and I would have to say a 40 year old virgin. Every girl he looked at was a potential wife. There was Vishal Gandhi who was just a little over 5 feet, thin and wore glasses. Ideal description of a geek? He was the biggest bully in the class. Then there was Bhatti (furnace), so called because he was as dark as the inside of a furnace. When enrolling into DJSCOE, Bhatti thought that it was a dance school. At every opportunity he got he would try to show off his dance skills. He was really good too, but doing the worm on a filthy dusty ground wasn't exactly the best way to showcase his skills. No matter what their flaws, some of these guys were the nicest people I have ever met in my life, and I will always respect them.

We had football practice every morning, and then there were tournaments as a result of which I missed a lot of lectures, so a meeting with the Head of the Department was inevitable. When I gave him the above-mentioned reason for missing classes, his exact words were, *"What are you going to do by playing football? Who are you trying to be, Sachin Tendulkar?"* I really wanted to be a wise guy and tell him, "Though I have chosen the wrong sport to emulate Sachin, I might just be able to do it with your blessing". But one thing you learn since you are a toddler in India is that you never ever make wise cracks to your teachers. They will screw you so bad that your next ten generations will be afraid to speak up to a teacher. A very good example on this front would be my friend Vishal Gandhi. Gandhi, as he was called, was not one of the favorite students amongst the teachers, along with me. Both of us were considered a taboo to the class. Teachers thought we were instrumental in getting down the class average.

However, though I was not the ideal student, I always kept a low profile to avoid confrontation with any teacher. Gandhi on the other hand had an 'I don't care a f***' attitude. Teachers in India are very easy to provoke too for some reason. You don't get up to greet them when they enter, you are screwed. You eat/drink during a lecture without permission, you are screwed. They might even get angry if you fart without permission. And Gandhi was quite the rebel, so it was no secret that teachers did not like him.

During one of our oral examinations, Gandhi and I were to go in together. Oral examinations have an internal examiner, i.e. from our college itself, and an external one. Usually in these exams, the internal tries their level best to help the students while the external usually asks tough questions. We sat down and the questions started to flow. I was my usual self, answering nothing. Gandhi on the other hand answered quite a few of the questions. I was genuinely surprised that he was so well prepared for the orals. After Gandhi and I stepped out, we were both very confident; him of getting decent marks in the orals, and me flunking and having to give it again. The examiners usually help the students and give them passing marks at least even if they did not answer any questions, something I was hoping for. The results came out and I got passing grades while Gandhi had been failed. Just a small example of what teachers can do if they don't like you in India. Internal examiners never wanted to take my orals. They knew it would be embarrassing for them.

Once Bhatti and I were the ones to go in first. One teacher was so paranoid that he told us that we should not go first as it spoils the reputation of the whole class. If only I could have sued him for that. But then again, when you think about my track record in orals, I would say it is a fair thing to say. There was a time when I was asked the full form of a subject that people usually said in its abbreviated form, and I answered incorrectly. Once the external examiner could not stop laughing after each answer Bhatti and I gave, and he ended up teaching half of the subject to us during the exam itself. During thermodynamics orals, I was asked what would be the elements I would take into consideration while purchasing an air conditioner. Expecting a strictly technical answer, she was dumbfounded when I replied, "I would look at how much it can cool the room".

Apart from the time when it came to taking oral and written exams, I was having a blast. Football and beer pretty much made up most of my daily activities. Also, I missed being in a relationship. I am not sure if it was the actual relationship that I missed, or just the physical benefits of being in one. I looked around but could not find anyone. Desperate times call for desperate measures. Vanita was not the best looking girl around. As a matter of fact, she was not really what you would classify as good looking. Standing at barely 5 feet, she was short and plum. The only thing I would say she had going for her was nice hair. We both had the same phone carrier,

Reliance, and so messaging was free for us. We used to message each other time and again and one day after a few drinks I messaged her saying she should give me a shot at being her boyfriend. In my head, this was just a simple message of which the answer was obviously going to be yes. To my surprise, she said she was not interested. To put things into perspective here, let me bring out the ladder for attractiveness out again. I would like to reiterate here that I do not consider myself very good looking; however, I know where I stand. And if Vanita and I were to take our spots on the ladder, I would be at least a couple of floors, not steps, above her. And this girl just turned me down? Apparently she was into fair men! And we all thought America had an issue with racism. I would again have to blame this fascination towards fair people on the society than her. In India, the concept of tall, dark and handsome is somehow lost. Girls are looking for guys who are tall, smart and fair. Guys are looking for tall and fair women. Parents with dusky/dark daughters are worried about no guy wanting to marry their daughter. If everyone wants fair people, what in the world will happen to all the people with a higher concentration on melanin in their skin?

I took this rejection as a challenge. There was no way a rejection from her was going down in my track record. I had to change the verdict. I had to fight for the rights of dark people to find someone, to be accepted. I had to be the next Martin Luther King Jr. So I did whatever it took. I became her best friend; I was always there for her. Free messaging meant we spoke late into the night via sms. Monthly I used to send a minimum of 2000 messages. I became so proficient that I could type without looking at the keypad, and do it faster than others typing the same text with their eyes fixed on the phone. Time and again I would try to convince her as to how good a guy I was and how I would make the perfect boyfriend. Then something happened. The results of second year came out and she had failed in a subject from first year again, and according to the rules she could not carry forward a subject from the first year to the third year. This meant she had to repeat the entire second year again. She was devastated. She could not stop crying after the results were out. This was my shot. She was depressed and I had to strike when the iron was hot. Yes, I know it is the worst thing to do but think about all the time I wasted here without any rewards. I had to play it dirty. And so I did. I asked her to come for a nice walk with me to "take her mind off things". We went to a coffee shop by the sea, talked for an hour. It was a beautiful setting with slight rain and just enough wind to make it a very romantic scene. Of course, I wasn't exactly looking for romance per se but the ambience definitely didn't hurt. We sat outside for a while in the rain, talking, contemplating on how she should deal with things. I had to be in. Though I knew I should not make a move right then, I was sure this would leave a lasting impression on her; enough to finally agree to go out with me. I drove her back home, and we spoke again for a long time via messaging at night. I took a chance and asked her out again, and this time she said yes. I had done it. I had broken the social barrier. The next morning I got a message from her saying she was sorry and that she was just caught up in the moment the previous night, and that she could not go out with me. I could not believe it. I decided to let this stupid woman be and look elsewhere for a "relationship".

By the end of my second year, Narayan and his school friends were planning a trip to Kerala. I knew all his school friends well by that time, and I decided to go along with them. It would be a good change for me from running around women, and football. Though I had been to Kerala many times, I had never been to the places we planned to visit. It was exciting. We all met up at the train station, all 6 of us; Akash aka Akki, Narayan aka Dodo, Jayaram aka Nanga, Pradeep aka Kallu, Siddharth aka Dean, and of course me. We boarded the train, and right next to us there was a pretty decent looking girl with her family. All of us looked at each other and smiled. Apart from Kallu*, all of us were single. So all the while in the train I kept trying to think of ways to talk to this girl. I could not just say hi and start talking because her parents were right there, and her dad looked a bit scary to be honest. I forgot about that for the moment and decided to enjoy the train ride. If any of you has not taken the train from Mumbai to Goa or back, you don't know what you are missing out on. When the train passes through Goa, some of the views are just breathtaking. We would be sitting at the door, with our jaws literally dropping with every passing mountain or valley. I can only compare that train journey to the drive through the Rocky Mountains.

Once we reached Kerala, we were to stay at Kallu's house, and right next door lived his grandparents. His grandparents are the coolest grandparents I have ever met. I really wished they would have adopted me. The house we had

*Pradeep is now happily married to the same girl Kamakshi. It is wonderful when relationships last.

to live in was huge. It had enough rooms for all of us to have an individual room, though we all decided to sleep in the hall like a nice big slumber party. Nanga and Dean had never had beer before. So we decided to go get a couple of beers, but a couple turned to 12. 12 bottles of beer in India are a lot. These are not small bottles of Heineken or as light as Miller light. These are like bottles of Steel Reserve, and we had just bought 12 of them. So with Dodo and Kallu watching as they did not drink, we started what turned out to be a very funny night. Dean and Nanga got drunk pretty fast as it was their first time. I was getting there too with a couple of beers down, while Akki was just gulping it down like water. And then the conversations began. We started talking about the girl on the train. I had found out that her dad was at a high post in the police. So I started telling my friends how I could be falsely accused of some crime and be locked up in prison for dating a policeman's daughter. To this the now drunk Nanga says, "You don't worry man. If you face any problems, my dad works for Tata". Yeah that definitely reduces my worries because working for a steel company means you can totally influence the police. I wanted to break a bottle on his head for saying that but then I remembered his dad worked for Tata.

Dean, in the meantime, started giving me advice on relationships. He told me I should give up my promiscuous ways and be serious with some girl. This was relationship advice coming from a guy who had never been in a relationship. Then I started talking about how I missed my brother, who had gone to America to pursue his masters. For the first time, I cried thinking about my brother that night.

Alcohol does two things to you, makes you emotional and makes you horny. As there were no women around, I had to settle for emotional. By the time we finished 12 bottles of beer, I had thrown up a couple of times and poor Kallu had to clean it. I don't remember going to sleep but do remember waking up with the worst hangover I had ever had. We tried out a lot of authentic Malayali food while we were there. Apparently, Kallu's grandfather was a well-known figure all around town, and wherever we went we had the best seats and the best service. The food was so good everywhere that Dean even asked at a couple of restaurants if it was possible for him to take some back to Mumbai. Much to his dismay, they said the food would go bad by the time it reached there. The rest of our trip included a lot more bottles of beer, more good food, and tennis for some reason. But all in all it was a great trip. Our train journey back was not as eventful as the one to Kerala, but again the views kept us from getting bored.

Going back to college after a nice long trip was a drag. Actually, going to college every time was a drag. But at that time there was something that we all, read desperados, had to look forward to; the fresher's party. Every year the college would organize this for the juniors to get to know the seniors. From the news I had heard, there were a lot of juniors I would want to be familiar with. I have told you before that good-looking people are a rare commodity in engineering colleges. So even if a mediocre looking girl comes in, she is treated like the next Miss Universe. And apparently the new crop of engineers had many of them. So it was worth going for this year's party. We did our ritual of going to the bar next to the college to have a couple of pints of vodka, followed by chicken fried rice. We entered the college looking around like a pack of wolves looking for their prey. There were some pretty new faces. Though everyone was looking for a tall, fair and well-endowed girl, my demands were a bit different. I always have, and always will, had a thing for dusky petite women. And that was exactly what I was looking for. Then I saw her. Well actually I think the whole crowd was looking at her. She was wearing a top with just laces at the back, with nice tight jeans that showed off her perfect buttocks. I was intrigued. Usually girls that look good from the back view are pathetic when it comes to the front view. So I was a bit skeptical, and decide to suspend my judgment. And then she turned. For a change, this girl was actually good looking from front too, not just from an engineering point of view, but in general too this girl would be considered good looking. I have to admit I was impressed. I will never say it was love at first sight, according to me there is no such thing. The "love" you feel at first sight is nothing but a physical attraction; to be more precise, something you feel in your pants. I did feel something in my pants but I wanted to learn more about this girl. With some good old-fashioned spy work, I found out that her name was Shilpa, and that she drank alcoholic beverages and she smoked. I smoked whenever I had drinks but somehow a girl smoking was a big turn off for me. And so were overrated people. And this girl was slowly getting overrated. Everyone was talking about every move this girl was making. I made a pact to myself to not give Shilpa any sort of attention whatsoever. If only I knew what the future held for me.

Anecdote : The Hangover

The year was 2004. FC Porto and Monaco were to contest the finals of the UEFA Champions League. It was to be an exciting match considering both teams were not expected to reach the finals. I really wanted to watch it but unfortunately I had a semester exam the very next day. I could not let an exam spoil the Champions League final for me. So I decided to go to Baggy's place in the evening so that he could teach me some topics before the game started at midnight. I got there around 8pm and he started teaching me immediately. By 10pm, we decided to take a break and have a beer. This is never a good idea. One beer led to another and soon we had some of his friends' over and they had a jam session. Before I knew it, the game had started and I was still drinking. By the end of the match, which Porto won, I was completely drunk and could not study anymore. I decided to drive back in my inebriated state anyway. As soon as I got home, I felt like I was going to hurl and so I ran to the toilet. As I was throwing up all my dinner and beer, my folks woke up concerned about me puking on the eve of my exam. My mom started asking me all these questions as to why I was vomiting and the best excuse I could come up with was, "I think it was the bad Chinese food I had for dinner". And they bought it! I could not believe my luck. I went to sleep hoping that I could get up early and study till afternoon for my exam. However, the morning after is never good when you have had so much. I had the worst headache possible. I could not even lift my head up. My mom gave me a few pain-killers which definitely helped with the pain, but left me too drowsy to study. So I went for the exam unprepared and with a hangover. I still don't remember what I wrote in that paper, but I managed to pass that exam with a bare minimum of 40 marks. Guess hangovers aren't that bad after all.

God's own country

Right before my third year of engineering, I had to go to Kerala once again. However, this time it was a family trip, which meant no drunken revelry, or so I thought. As usual, the frugal South Indians that we were, we decided to travel by train, as the trip was more "enjoyable" like that. To be honest, I would rather travel to Kerala by train than by flight if time permits. The reason being that, though flight saves about 24 hours of travel, it is just plain boring. Also, the whole atmosphere in an airplane is kind of morose. You can almost feel people around you praying that there be no technical glitches, or have any hijackers*.

To add to the tension, the signs on a plane do not help lighten the situation much. I personally believe there should be some dark humor inside the cabin just to ease the tension. For example:

"Only Pilots and Hijackers are allowed inside the cockpit. Others will be prosecuted."

"Seat-belts save lives. If the person next to you is annoying you, remove his/her seat-belt."

"Pilots will give you useless information during the flight. Do not pay attention."

"If there is an emergency, the oxygen masks will drop. Every man for himself."

*A guy hijacking a plane to Kerala has to be working for Emirates airlines. Can you imagine the number of people who would have to fly back and forth for the funerals from Dubai?

"Children who cry will be thrown out mid-flight."

You get the gist. Unfortunately, not everyone thinks alike and as a result planes are boring and trains are not. On a train, you can interact with a lot of people, and walk around to stretch your legs, and soak in the beautiful scenery. There are two drawbacks however. First and foremost, when one Malayali meets another Malayali, they have to bond. It just comes naturally to our kind. We feel this sense of pride to meet another one from the beautiful state. As much as I do it myself, I am very selective about whom I bond with and people above a certain age are definitely not my foray.

Second, and more important, drawback is the restroom. Toilets in Indian trains, apart from Rajdhani, are horrible. To begin with, the stench is intolerable. Add to that the fact that the train keeps moving side-to-side doesn't help your balance much, especially while using an Indian style toilet. Of all the things I respect my brother for, I respect him the most for his control over his bowel movements. He could actually sit in the train for 2 whole days without using the restroom even once. That is some serious talent.

My parents and I reached our place in Kerala after a long tiring journey. The whole point of this journey was a cousin's marriage. I was excited to meet my cousin as I had not met him since he had left for Dubai a few years back. We decided to catch up over a couple of drinks. As an engineering student, I was perpetually broke. And him being a Pizza Hut employee in Dubai, I didn't want him to spend the little bit of savings he had either. So we decided to have local *desi daaru*. This was the first time I was going to try this form of alcohol and it kind of scared me a bit. After a couple of drinks though, that fear was replaced by what I can only describe as joy. After a few drinks, he was supposed to take me to his would-be wife's house. We reach there and he introduced me to his girl or a blob, as I would like to refer to her. I had met the blob as a kid and from what I remembered she was a good-looking kid. Unfortunately, she turned into a kid who ate her emotions, and everyone around her. I started wondering why my cousin was doing this to himself. From what I knew of him, he did not have a fetish of such kind. My curiosity began to get the better of me and I started some good old-fashioned spying. I casually asked my cousin if he was getting any dowry for the marriage. Though he initially denied it, he later told me that the girl's father was giving my uncle enough money to pay of my uncle's debts. My uncle was using his son to pay off his debts! If he had planned it better, and had maybe 5-6 kids, he would have been a millionaire*.

The wedding was a much boring affair. You see South Indian weddings have nothing but a guy sitting and reading *mantras* while the bride and groom are sitting next to the "holy" fire, and the whole crowd is gathered around them. Can you imagine two South Indians, one with Arsonphobia and the other with Claustrophobia trying to get married? Now that would be one exciting marriage. Coming back to my cousin's ceremony, he was aptly dressed in a white shirt and a white *mundu*. However, the blob went all out in a red sari that hurt my eyes. Well, looking at her was enough to hurt my eyes. She could have gone straight from the marriage hall to a Halloween party and she would have fit right in. As soon as the ceremony was over, and after everyone threw grains of rice

My family planning began that day.

enough to satiate the hunger of Somalia, the rush to the hall serving food began and man was there a rush. You may have seen stampedes when large crowds are gathered for an event and something goes wrong. But nothing compares to the stampede when Malayalis are rushing for free food.

As family, unfortunately, we were supposed to wait till the very end to eat with the bride and groom. As I saw the blob devour her food, I realized that this was a marriage made in heaven. My cousin was happy because he finally got someone who agreed to marry him, and the blob was happy because she was getting married to someone working at pizza hut. Free pizzas for life!

Unfortunately the celebrations died down sooner than they began as my maternal grandfather was admitted to the hospital. We, as a family, were always closer to our mother's family. My father had fallen out with his family a long time back and we were out of touch with that side since childhood. As a result, every time we visited Kerala, we would be at my mother's childhood home with her parents, my uncles and aunts, our cousins and it would be a blast. This time as well, all of the younger generation was present for the wedding. The news of our grandfather being admitted took us all by surprise. I will not lie and say that my relationship with my grandfather was great. But it was not bad either. Meeting him only once a year did not exactly help bolstering our relationship; however, I was always excited to be there. We definitely had our ups and downs. I particularly remember this once incident where my cousins and I had just come back after a tiring session of cricket and switched on the fan in our room. My grandfather barged in and switched it off saying that it was not meant for us to enjoy after playing cricket. Summers in Kerala are not exactly the kindest, and having to sit there without fans was just too much to handle and we lost our cool, in more ways than one. So we hatched a brilliant plan to get back at Grandpa. One of my cousins switched off the main. As power cuts were usual, no one really thought much of it. Then I went into each and every room and turned on every switch in sight, even if some of them didn't do anything. As soon as my cousin got the signal from me, he put the main back on. And all of a sudden, every light, fan, and electrical appliance in the house was on. My grandfather quickly caught on to our little prank. He charged at us with his walking stick. It was surprising to see a man who required a walking stick to walk, run so fast with the stick raised up like a sword.

When my grandfather was admitted, the family which had just seen a "joyous" event suddenly turned morose. To be honest, I was a bit confused primarily because he had been admitted a couple of times before and he had been back home in a couple of days. But this time, everyone was worried. I suppose everyone but I knew the severity of his condition. For us from the younger generation, it more or less meant spending more time with our cousins whom we usually met once a year, if at all. And this time, apart from my brother, each and every one of us was there. And did I mention that all of us are male? You can imagine the chaos when 9 guys meet up after a long time. It was utter chaos. We tried to make the most of the situation. In a way, it was good to have all of them around because I completely forgot about my grandfather being in the hospital. We were so engrossed in hatching plans against each other, or playing cricket, that we forgot about the bigger picture. However, one phone call was soon to bring it all to our attention.

I remember it was a bright sunny afternoon. My cousins and I were out playing cricket as usual. One of our parents would always be at the hospital and they would call at regular intervals to inform the others of my granddad's condition. That day, after one of these calls, my uncle who was at the hospital called back within 5 minutes. As we did not have a phone connection at that point, all calls were made to the neighbor's house. No sooner had the neighbor informed us of the second call, the whole household burst into tears. I was dumbfounded. Why are all these women crying when it is just a second call? Maybe my uncle had just forgotten to mention something in the previous call. My dad ran to answer the phone, and with a few minutes got back with news justifying all the tears that had been shed in the last 5 minutes. My grandfather had passed away.

As soon as the news hit, the crying became louder and the chest thumping became harder from all the women in the house. My grandmother completely broke down. I had never seen her like that. She was, and still is, a jovial person whom we still make fun of and she takes it ever so well, just like she always did. My mother and her two sisters were sobbing uncontrollably, while her two brother, my uncles were planning how to go about the ceremonies. Amidst all this, the first thought that came into my head was, "Does this mean we have to stop playing cricket for the remaining days I was there?"

I have no clue why this was the only thing I could think of. Maybe I just did not want to think about the fact that my grandfather had just passed away. This was the first time someone whom I knew so well had died. My father's dad has passed away even before I was born, while his mother whom we had definitely spent some good time with passed away when I was quite young. For me, this was the first of such incidents since I had sort of grown up. And I was not exactly sure how to deal with the situation.

The body was got back to the house that day itself, and kept in the living room. I saw my uncles break down for the first time. I was taken aback. It made me think at that point if I would ever care about someone so much that I would burst out in tears like that. I had in the past cried when Vedika had broken up with me. But when I looked back at that, it was not because I was in love with her. But because I was losing someone I could talk to. Because if she was not around, I would be lonely. My uncles were crying out of the love they had for their father. I started thinking at that time if I loved someone so much, or was I too selfish and cold to not care about anyone but me? As the news spread, more and more people started visiting the house, and the mourning continued throughout the night. The younger generation was asked to sleep early but it was a bit hard for me to close my eyes with a dead body in the next room. I do not mean to disrespect my grandfather in any way by referring to him merely as a dead body but isn't that what we are all reduced to in the end? As I have mentioned before, I have always been scared of ghosts. Even the pathetic movies and shows by Ramsay brothers would send a chill down my spine. So sleeping that night was not the easiest of tasks to say the least.

The following day, a *pujari* came to say different *mantras* while one of my uncles performed rituals around my grandfather's corpse. As soon as they were done with that, the body was carried to the backyard where a deep rectangular hole had been dug. I suddenly realized that he was going to be buried, and not cremated. As per Hindu rituals, once a person passes away, the body is to be cremated. But this was not the case here. This was definitely not going to help my sleep much in that house. The casket was slowly lowered into the grave and slowly it was covered with dirt. Soon my grandfather was under a pile of rubble and dirt.

The remaining days in God's Own Country were more or less a drag. You wouldn't exactly expect much after what had happened. Everyone left one by one apart from my mom's elder sister who was to stay with my grandmother. Mine was the last family to leave the house. I took one last long hard look at my grandfather's grave. Everyone thought it was out of love, but it was more to just see what might become of me one day. Let me tell you, that thought was scary. Soon I was on the train back to Mumbai, to get back to an uninteresting life of alcohol, football, and a couple of books.

Me? An Engineer? Part 2

By the third year of engineering, I was known around college as a football player. I didn't know if I should be taking it as a compliment. It did not necessarily mean I was good at it, it just meant people only saw me doing that. Before exams if anyone saw me in the library, they would ask me if I actually ever had a library card made. So I was not considered a genius I suppose. Apart from this, I was also kind of known as Rehan's lover. Rehan was a guy I met when I tried out for the football team in my first year, and he at that time was in his second year. He was one of those guys, like me, who didn't know too many people around so I tried talking to him but this guy was really an introvert and I could not get him to talk much, as opposed to all the yapping I do. I can seriously talk a lot. I am worse than women talking about bags and shoes, guys talking about sex and the time wasted by Indians watching cricket. So considering that, it was a bit annoying that after all the talking I did, this guy was not responding much. So I decided not to try anymore. But one fine day I get a call at my house. As soon as I picked it up, the person on the other side said, "We are playing football below my building. Do you want to come?" This is a problem with most Indians. The other person is supposed to know who you are from your voice. Nowadays, you call people on their cell phones, or landlines have caller ids so that they know who is calling. But back in the day that was not the case. I didn't have a mobile phone till the third year of engineering, and my landline did not have a caller id. So how in the world would I know who is calling? I am no psychic people. Just say who is calling so that I don't start talking dirty with you on the phone.

Now when I got that call, I was unsure as to what I should do or say because I had no clue who it was and I did not want to insult the person. So thinking I was very smart, I replied, "Oh sure I would love to. Give me your address." To which the person on the phone replies, "Come on man you know my place." WTF! The result was a long complicated conversation; and at the end of talking to him for around 15 minutes I asked, "So who is this?" It was Rehan, and we were very close friends ever since. So much so that someone sent him a red rose on Rose Day on my behalf, which I was made to hand it to him in front of his class.

Talking of Rose Day, what is with all the "Days" we celebrated, and still celebrate, in colleges in India? It is the most inane thing anyone could ever do, but all of us do it. Rose Day, when you give roses to people you like. If you give it on any other day you might be considered a freak, but on rose day it is cool to give a rose to someone. Then there is Traditional Day because usually we don't really care a f**k about our culture or tradition, but come Traditional Day and we all love to show off our roots. Mix 'n match Day where you wear weird combinations of outfits, and the weirder they are, the more cool points you score. Then there is Formal Day where men like to show potential mates how they look good in suits, while women like to show their prospective mates how good their cleavage looks in a dress. There are tons more which I do not want to get into but they are all more absurd than the other. As I am talking about the bizarre things we Indians do, let me talk about a couple more. We call every person elder to us 'Uncle' or 'Aunty'. I understand as kids we had a pledge in our textbooks that started off with "India is my country. All Indians are my brothers and sisters".

This does not necessarily mean everyone our age is actually our brothers and sisters, and hence, anyone elder to us would be our uncles and aunts. Whatever happened to etiquette? How about calling people 'Sir' or 'Madam'? We also have a tendency to mess up the English language. Apart from amalgamating Hindi and English which all of us do, there are these standard grammatical errors which everyone makes. It is like it has been passed on from generation to generation. For example, we all say, "Let me explain you". Let me explain you? Are you a shrink all of a sudden that you can now "explain me"? What happened to the preposition 'TO' in that sentence? Also, every Indian 'gives' exams/tests. How do you give an exam? You are not an examiner to 'give' an exam to the student. You 'take' an exam as students. I am no Shakespeare, and I make tons of grammatical errors, some of them you might even find in this book. However, I just felt it is important to point out the errors that we as a nation make so that the future generations won't do the same. Last but not the least, and my favorite thing that Indians do is something we see in Indian movies. When a pregnant woman's water breaks, she is admitted in a hospital. After lying in the bed, moaning for a while, the doctor comes in with a stethoscope, checks the heart rate, then the pulse, and announces that she is ready to deliver the baby. Like Tim Allen would say on the show Home Improvement, "Back the pregnancy truck up for a minute". What happened to checking how much the woman has dilated? So even if she has dilated only a couple of centimeters, she is ready to deliver because the heat rate definitely seems to indicate she is ready. Maybe in real life doctors in India don't look at the vagina of women because it is a sacred region of the body for Indians. But we do not seem to think so when we are pounding the shit out of the "sacred region" to become the second largest population in the world. Man I love India.

After that long digression, let me get back to third year of engineering. Rehan and I did everything together, be it drinking, playing football, or hitting on women. Of course we wouldn't hit on the same girl, but would talk to each other about whom we would like to hit on and how to go about it. Once we got the not so difficult task of selecting the girls' badminton team for DJSCOE, and we picked girls we wanted to hit on, and completely ignored the better players. I still wonder why no one ever complained about the selection criteria. Rehan was more forward with the girl he wanted to hook up with than I was with mine unfortunately. So he got some action while I came back to the almighty hand. But I was never jealous. In fact, I was very happy for him. That was the kind of friendship we had. At that time, he was the captain of the football team, and we had a great season that year. During one of the games, the whole team was talking about how hot Shilpa was. I tried to stay out of the conversation considering my view on overhyped people. But one of the guys asked me what I thought, and I decided to go with the flow and told everyone I found her hot too. One of my teammates then told me that I should add her on MSN Messenger because she adds everyone anyway. So I thought about it, conferred with Rehan, and decided to go ahead and add her. What possible harm could come out of having a beautiful girl on my list of friends?

And even if she told me I am a total loser and never spoke to me again it would not make a difference because no one really knew me as such apart from people involved in sports.

I decided to go all in. I added her, and every day since, I would be a bit nervous to go on MSN. One fine day, I went on MSN and as soon as I logged in I got an instant message. It was her, Shilpa. She asked me if she knew me. I was perplexed. I had no clue what to say. So I decided to go with, "I am from DJSCOE as well. I know you, and I think you know me as well". What followed was a number of guesses on her part, which were all obviously wrong because she did not know of my existence anyway. Then I decided to give her a hint and told her I was the Sports Secretary of the college. To my surprise, she said she had heard about me, and had even seen me a couple of times! My heart definitely skipped a few beats. The best-looking girl in college knew of my existence*. From that day onwards, we spoke online every day. It was great. We spoke for hours, spoke about everything under the sun, and I even got her number. But I preferred to talk online because it was just easier. After a while, I started getting the feeling that this girl was kind of into me, which got me all the more excited. One day, she told me that we should meet up. It was a scary thought. You see talking online is a piece of cake for me, or for anyone. As a matter of fact, my online conversational skills are so brilliant, I have impressed more than a few women by just talking to them online. But talking to someone in person is a whole new ball game. You have all the time in the world when it comes to talking online. You can think of witty replies. But in person, you have to be spontaneous, and I am

*Wow, I was such a loser.

anything but. But again coming to the ladder theory, if a person above you on the ladder wants to meet you, you never say no. So I went ahead and met her at Barista. It was late in the evening and she had to be home soon. So instead of sitting at a stupid coffee shop, I decided to give her a ride home. The half-an-hour drive was great. We picked up from where we had left off online and continued talking. After I dropped her home, she texted me saying it was great to meet me and that we should meet more often. The end of the third year could not have been better.

Come fourth year, and I got some bad news. Well, actually it was good news, but it just made me sad. Rehan had decided to go to the USA to pursue his masters, and be one of the PIGS. After spending 3 whole years with a very good friend, he was not going to be around anymore. It sucked. But I was still happy for him. A few days before he was to leave India to join the University of Southern California, we decided to go to the restaurant he owned in Vasai, and have a good time. In all there were 8 of us who went there. We knew from the beginning we did not have to pay for anything. So we drank the best Indian scotch, Black Dog, and ate the best appetizers on the menu. All of us were hammered, and I think I even shed a few tears by the end of the night because some of those assholes kept pestering me, asking me how I felt about him leaving and finally I gave in to peer pressure and told them how I felt.

The ones that were comparatively less drunk decided to drive while the rest of us, like me who would not be able to stand straight at that time if their life depended on it, decided to sit behind. But motion sickness is a bitch when you are drunk. I am sure I left a trail of puke from his restaurant to his cousin's restaurant which was a 45 min drive. We decided to stop at his cousin's restaurant because it was a point where from all of us would be going in different directions to get back home. As soon as we stopped there, I hurled more right in front of that restaurant. One of the restaurant's waiters quickly got a bucket of water to clean the mess, however a stray dog was quicker in eating the entire mess up. That was definitely one of the most disturbing sights I have ever seen in my life, after Two Girls One Cup and BME Pain Olympics. A few days later we went to the airport to see Rehan off. After he went, I was left pondering as to how I would actually enjoy my remaining days in college. But to my relief I did not have to spend all of my last one year in college. The first 6 months of final year for production engineering students meant going on an internship. Godrej was one of the first companies to come to college to interview potential interns. I aced the test and got through. Again, I had mixed feeling about working at Godrej. I was happy for not having to go to college for 6 months but I was also a bit sad that I would not get time to spend with Shilpa just when we were really beginning to hit it off.

For our first day at Godrej, Gandhi and I decided to take the bus together to get there. We reached on time, which was 7am (#%$*&), and sat through the orientation yawning. Apparently, I had scored the highest in the written test and so I was placed in the tool room, one of the leading tool rooms in Asia. I was excited to start. We were taken to meet the people we would be working under, and I was to work under Mr.

Negi, the manufacturing head of the plant, and one of the nicest human beings alive. He took me to the automated machines section, a room on its own and told me that was where I had to work. After 5 minutes of sitting in the room, I realized that the room was a bit too cold. So much so, that my tits could cut through diamonds at that time. But I did not complain. It was better than working outside the room where it was super hot. All the while I was there, I kept texting Shilpa, telling her what was happening. After just a week of working, I was already cranky about getting up at 7am for 6 days a week. Yes, 6 days a week. People in India usually work on Saturdays too. Forget long weekends, regular weekends were once in a fortnight. So I decided to skip one day as we got 13 paid leaves anyway, and decided to go to DJ instead and meet Shilpa. She was pleasantly surprised to see me. She bunked her lecture and we went for a walk. It was raining but that did not deter us from taking that walk. We had a cup of hot tea from a small stall right next to the college, and then walked in the rain for almost an hour before deciding to head back. It was like puppy love all over again. She told me that she was contesting for a committee position in IEEE, and that she would find out about it the next day. The next day when I was at work, I texted her asking about it, and she told me she didn't get the position and was upset. Trying to show how considerate I was, after work as soon as I reached home, I drove to her place and told her I was downstairs and that we should go have a cup of coffee so that she would feel better. However, things did not quite go as they did when I thought of this in my head.

Let me tell all you guys, never ever try to be nice to a woman. Women are retards who like bad boys. It is a well-known fact and I am reiterating that point. Why women cant like nice guys is quite a conundrum alright. Maybe it is because nice guys might treat them too nicely, give them everything they need. What a dilemma. And Shilpa was the same, just like any other moron of the opposite sex. Not only did she not come downstairs to meet me that day, she started avoiding me as much as she could; apparently I was too "nice" now. We were supposed to go for a movie to which she reluctantly agreed. We were inside the theatre when we saw a girl from our college, who was one of the models in the college fashion show with Shilpa, and Shilpa spent the whole time in the theatre hiding herself, making sure she was not seen with me in public. It was a sting for the ego, but I decided to hang around and be her friend for a while. Within a month, I find out that she was dating someone else, a bad boy I would like to call Mr. Palindrome. Mr. Palindrome was a short, chubby boy who was apparently better than me for some reason. To the naked eye, you could not see it. Maybe there was more to him than being able to read his name backwards, or the extra flab. I decided to let it go and just avoid giving Shilpa any more attention. But this is when women are the most annoying. They might reject you, but once you start ignoring them, they start talking to you like you mean the world to them. The exact same thing happened with Vanita as well. Even though I wasn't really trying for her anymore, we used to talk quite a bit. Once I started talking to Shilpa more and more, she got really insecure and sent me messages saying she missed talking to me. Shilpa, too, started messaging me on MSN and texting me more frequently. How much attention do you women need?

Apart from having to deal with annoying women in my life, working at Godrej was anything but fun. Apparently, interns are not really engineers and so are given jobs like copying and printing, tracking lost jobs, and forwarding emails. Mr. Negi was a very religious man and every time he would get one of those emails with a photo of one of the million Gods we have in India, he had to forward it to many people and he did not know how to. Maybe he knew too but just thought I was there anyway so why not use me to do all the dirty work. I would get so bored working there some days that I would end up taking a nap in one of the western style bathrooms. Yeah a nap and I am not ashamed to say I would be sitting on the commode for that. Imagine how boring your work would be if taking a nap, whilst sitting on a commode, was the best part of your eight hour shift. One of the supervisors there, Mr. Joshi, knew I was up to something funny. Every time he looked for me, I was nowhere to be found. In between all these days of napping hard, I found out that Mr. Palindrome had left to be one of the PIGS. Was this another opportunity that God was giving me with Shilpa? Was this meant to be?

Trying my luck again with her would mean sacrificing any self-respect I had left. But then again, it meant having a shot at dating a good-looking girl. I weighed my options, and self-respect seemed somewhat less of a priority. I had to get the timing and the message right. I had not spoken properly to this girl for a while now, and I could not just barge into her life again. So I waited and I waited; till I got drunk the next time. I was sitting at a friend's place in my colony/apartment complex. It was almost 1:00am and we were all buzzed to say the least. The amount of drinks you have is directly proportional to the courage you have to talk to a girl. So I was in a confident mood and I decided to text her saying how I missed talking to her. Though I was not expecting a reply right then, I got one from her saying how she did not like how things were left hanging either. So we were back to square one. Though we did not talk as much as we used to, we definitely kept in touch. I could have tried to hit on her but she had made it very clear that she was still seeing Mr. Palindrome. I have never got the concept of long distance relationships. You are never around when your partner needs you, emotionally or physically.

How will it ever work? Many people say that physical needs aren't as important as emotional needs. Physical needs are way more important according to me as I have mentioned earlier. Emotionally you have to be compatible of course, but would any girl be with a guy who cannot ever make her get an orgasm? Or would a guy ever be with a girl who is just not good in bed? A physical relationship is very important, and there is nothing physical with a long distance relationship. However, a bit later on I did find out that Mr. Palindrome had issues with holding his pee pee up for more than 5 minutes. So I guess it was rational to be in a long distance relationship. You were not getting laid when he was around, so why bother when he is not!

Months passed with Shilpa and I being friends. Her birthday was approaching fast, and I had to give something thoughtful. That way I hoped I would have my foot in the door. I decided to make her a website. Not an actually hosted website, one of those free ones. I was still a student, and so I was always broke; don't judge. I made a few pages with one for her friends, one her family, one what I thought about her (purely plutonic statements), and the home page described her. She was thrilled to see it. She went on to show it to all her friends, including Mr. Palindrome who thought I was a loser to make it. But this loser's position as a friend had definitely changed after that; I had moved up the hierarchy. Things were moving slowly, but that was something. Since her birthday, we started talking every day. Talking about how our day was, how some movie coming on TV was good or bad*, and also about how things were not going well with Mr. Palindrome, which is always a good sign. Months went by quickly and it was time for the college festival again. Shilpa decided not to participate in the fashion show that year because one of her stalkers got into the fashion show by getting a few sponsors. And then he wrote a note in his book which all of us got to read because of some good old spy work. This was what the note said:

"I finally did it. I am in the fashion show, and I will walk next to Shilpa, the GODDESS. I will stand right next to her, holding her hand and the whole world will watch me in envy."

Come the day of the fashion show and Shilpa, I, and a few other friends went in to watch. While we were inside, there was this cute girl standing with the so-called "security" head, Mr. Patel, also a student of the college. Shilpa challenged me to go talk to the girl which I promptly accepted and went outside the

*I always asked her opinion first before I gave my opinion. It is always important to agree during the initial stages.

make-shift barricade to talk to the girl. After my unsuccessful attempt to get her to tell me her name, as I was getting back in, the diminutive 4'5" frame of Mr. Patel came in front of me. Apparently, I was entering through the exit line. Considering there was no one around for miles, I just smiled and tried to go ahead anyway. But Patel was adamant and would not let me through. The alcohol in me prompted me to lift him up holding his shoulders and gently place him aside, which I did and went in.

The next day when Shilpa, I, and our mutual friend Vamsi were walking out of the college gates, Mr. Patel tapped me on the shoulder and asked me to take a little walk with him. I asked Shilpa to go home as she was getting late anyway and I went to talk to the little guy while Vamsi waited for me. As soon as I stood in front of Patel, around 15 guys surrounded me.

They were all there to beat me up because I had apparently broken Patel's glasses when I lifted him up the day before. Vamsi realized what was happening, and came running to my aid. He was told by the crowd that if he were to get involved, he would get beat up too. The true friend that he is, Vamsi backed away into the safety of the college. Then a guy from the crowd, who was as short and tiny as Patel if not shorter and tinier, comes up to me and tells me that as I touched his "brother" I would now have to get beat up. I tried reasoning but this new guy was immovable, and told me that as I was alone he would let me fight him one on one and no one else would touch me. Did he really think I am that stupid? I knew the minute I touch him, the 15 bimbos standing around me would beat the crap out of me. I could take this midget any day. In fact, I could have played with him like Bluto plays with Popeye before Popeye has his spinach. And in this case even if he had spinach, I would still kick his butt. But knowing the implications of laying a finger on any one of them, I did not do anything. Suddenly, someone yelled, "Let's get it over with". As soon as I heard that, I ducked and put my hands over my head. Then I felt a shower of fists on my back and as fast as they had surrounded me, they had all disappeared. My true friend Vamsi came back to help me. He had called Shilpa and told her what was happening. She was waiting for me close to my place to check on me. I met her and she started apologizing for some reason. Apparently, she was feeling guilty for asking me to go talk to the girl during the fashion show as a result of which I got manhandled. And from that day onwards, I got more attention from her! Mr. Patel I have just two words for you; "Fuck Thank you!"

As days went by, she started showing more interest in me. So much so that she even wanted to meet my SNFT group. SNFT stood for Saturday Night Full Tight. It was a group comprised of Sahil and Hasnain Zafar, Prasad, Stavros aka Jojo, Abhijeet aka Abu, Roy, James, Charmaine, and finally me. Every Saturday night we would meet at Toto's in Bandra to have a few drinks, get drunk and go sleep anywhere, be it roadside or somewhere in our colony. But we would always make it a point to get home before our folks woke up in the morning. Shilpa wanted to meet them and it was a big thing. The group was such that they loved to make fun of a new group member. Vanita once met them, and she literally ran away. So though I was skeptical, I decided to take Shilpa to our next SNFT meeting.

To my surprise, everyone absolutely loved her. Shilpa was a great sport and took everything lightly, which is what I suppose they were looking for. As I was driving her home that night, I told her how I really felt about her. Much to my dismay, she told me she still had feelings for Mr. Palindrome and that she was not over him. I was left heartbroken. But I decided to suppress any feelings I had as exams were coming up soon and these were my last exams in engineering and I had to do well. So the next month or so I studied really hard and focused on my books rather than Shilpa, though we would talk time and again. Most of the exams were over with and I had done pretty well in all of them. Only one paper was left, after a holiday, which was a subject on sales and marketing which only required a lot of crap to be written in the paper to get good grades. So I did not think twice when Shilpa called me over to her place that night to have a few drinks with a couple of her friends as her exams were done and dusted. We were all having a good time, joking and laughing. But as I told you guys before, when you get drunk you get really horny. I was sitting with three girls. One was Shilpa whom I had given up on; one was a girl I would never do anything with even if I was so drunk that I could not even see. And then there was Leena. Now Leena was again a girl past the 8-drink limit. According to Rehan, 8 drinks is the limit. After 8 drinks, each and every girl seems beautiful. I would have never found Leena attractive but I was way past the 8-drink mark and suddenly she was someone

I had to have that night.

I tried everything I could. At one point, I even told her, "I am an ass person, and I love your ass." I know it is the lamest pickup line ever but what do you expect when I was so hammered? Finally, we all decided to sleep over at Shilpa's place itself. I was sleeping next to Leena and pretty much convincing her to make out with me but this girl, apart from giving me a peck, kept telling me I was in love with Shilpa. I should have explained the ladder theory of looks to her right then but it was just too taxing. I decided to drive home at night itself and went into Shilpa's room to tell her I was leaving. She was lying on her bed and was almost asleep. I tapped her gently and told her I was leaving. She pulled my hand and asked me to just sleep over and leave the next day, and while doing so slid over to make room for me on the bed. So I lay down next to her and turned on my side facing her, while she had her back towards me. I placed my right hand over her shoulder and gently kissed the back of her head. At that moment, she turned around to face me. We were close, lips almost touching. Then we kissed. It was an amazing moment. It was not only extremely sensual, but also felt great because this was a girl I was falling for. I was kissing Shilpa!

The next morning, I got up early to go home, and also to avoid an awkward scenario. I kissed her goodbye and left. While I was studying, I got a call from Shilpa. She wanted to talk about the night before. Why do women always want to talk about things? Just be happy about it and let it go. But you people just love talking and spoiling it for us men. And so we talked about it, and turns out she did not want to be with me and that whatever happened last night was just in the spur of the moment. She made me promise not to tell anyone as she didn't want Mr. Palindrome to find out. This girl had just used me, and now I was not even allowed to boast about it. Being the gentleman I am, I decided to keep it a secret. Exams got over and the SNFT clan was planning a road trip to Lonavala. I invited Shilpa too, and she was more than excited when she heard about it. The night before we were supposed to leave for the trip, all of us, except Shilpa, met up at a cheap bar called Yacht in Bandra to have a few drinks. One drink led to another and soon we were sloshed. Prasad and Hasnain decided to stay over at my place, while the others went to Sahil's house. I had keys to my house so I opened the door as quietly as I could and led my friends into my room. As soon as they sat on my bed, my dad came in. To prevent myself from swaying in front of my dad, I decided to hold the frame of the door and stand in front of him. He could smell the alcohol off me and asked me why I was drunk. Until then, he had no clue that I used to drink outside the house which was a bit surprising considering I once showed him how to have flame shots. When I told him we hadn't been drinking, he asked Hasnain the same question. I obviously thought he would go with my story of not having had any drinks. But his reply was, "Uncle, first rain of the season. We had to celebrate!" My dad got really pissed off, and told me that I could not take the car next day for our trip. Considering mine was one of the two cars, the other being Abu's, we were to drive to Lonavala, this was a major setback. Next day I woke up before my folks did, and left with my friends in my car anyway.

On our way, we decided to pick up a bottle of Smirnoff twist, a bottle of Alcazar vodka, and a bottle of Old Monk rum. And the responsible people that we were, even decided to open it and have shots while on the highway towards Lonavala. Kids reading this book, please do not ever drink and drive. When I look back on those days, I realize how foolish and stupid I was. By the time we got to Lonavala, we were all buzzed. We stopped at this tourist spot there called Bushy Dam. It was a dam where people just jumped into the water, and parents played with their kids in the water. As we had finished the bottle of Smirnoff during the drive itself, we opened the bottle of Old Monk and started taking turns of taking a dip, then coming back out to take a shot. The second girl who was with us, Jenisha, was drinking for the first time in her life. Soon, she could not stand and we had to carry her to our car with everyone staring at us. From there, we quickly drove up a hill to another tourist spot called the Lions Point. Leaving Jenisha in the car, we sat down at the edge of the cliff and opened the bottle of Alcazar. It was a beautiful day with the sun out but with a nice cloud cover. We could see rain far away from us. For a minute, none of us spoke. We just stared into the distance, amazed at how beautiful this place was. Just as we were about to head back home, a 2 hour drive, Abu's car would not start and there was no way all 8 of us would be able to get into my small Maruti 800. So Shilpa called her dad who was at a high post in the police in Mumbai. Her dad then pulled a few strings and organized a pickup truck to tow Abu's car to the city where a mechanic would take care of it. As we were waiting for the tow truck to arrive, Shilpa was sitting really close to me. So I turned to her and she was looking at me too. So I leaned in to kiss her. She did not pull away immediately, but did so after a few seconds. She did not say or do anything; just looked at me, smiled, and walked away.

Soon the tow truck came and we were on our way down. I was driving my car. After all the drinking and lack of sleep, I was extremely tired and extremely sleepy. I kept yawning while following the tow truck. Suddenly, I hear Shilpa and Hasnain, who were in the car with me, yell "Anish!" I had dozed off. Luckily, the car veered to the side of the wall, and not the side that had the valley. Till we got down to the city, I managed to keep my eyes open. Shilpa's dad had even managed to book 3 rooms in a hotel for all of us so that we did not have to drive late in the night. Though we had 3 rooms for 8 people, all of us slept in one room, on one double bed, with one of us being Jojo who at that point was 120kgs (250 lbs.) light. We drove back home the next day. I did not want the trip to end because it was getting me closer to Shilpa. But as soon as she got home, she called me and told me how she missed me. At that point, I suggested that both of us should study for our GREs together at my place, which she agreed to. The very next day, she came over to "study". After studying for a bit, we decided to take a nap. But nap was the last thing we had on our mind at that point. We kissed again and this time no one pulled away. The rest of the day went in studying for an hour followed by some scenes which would be hidden behind flowers or trees in a Bollywood movie. I wonder why my GRE scores weren't that great. While driving her home, I asked her what all this meant. She said she did not want to be in a relationship right now, and just wanted things to be the way they were. This girl was rejecting me again! I was just disgusted, and she could see it. But who was I to say no to a beautiful girl who wanted to be 'friends with benefits' with me? So I made my peace with it and kept quiet. The next day, Shilpa came over again to study. We started kissing again but this time she stopped me. She looked at me and asked, "Would you like to go out with me?" At first I thought she wanted to go for lunch or dinner or something. But then I realized she was asking me to go steady with her. After all the strikes, I had finally hit a home run. That is how I started dating Ms. Shilpa Nair.

Anecdote : My most embarrassing moment

In 9th grade, I visited Kerala and my parents were taking me to a relative's place which was a good 4 hours in the bus. Within the first 10 minutes of the bus journey, I felt like taking a dump. Considering it was a non-stop bus for 4 hours I was getting desperate an hour in. I told my mom my problem and she frantically started searching for a seat in the bus. By the time she found a seat, the bus had started smelling and I sitting down would have been a bigger problem. And did I say I was in 9th grade during this "accident"? Considering these events, my most embarrassing moment has to be something special. And according to me, it was the first time I got a boner. I was a really young, and was watching a movie on TV with my brother. Suddenly the main characters start making love. I felt something in my pants. My little pee pee was getting hard. This completely freaked me out. I ran to my folks who were in the kitchen. I dropped my pants and showed them what was happening. My mom told me it might be because I wanted to urinate. So I went and stood in the toilet for a while with no avail. After 5 mins, I ran back to my mother and told her I didn't pee and it is still hard. My mom just smiled and asked me to sit down for a while and everything would be fine. Everything did turn out to be fine, apart from when I look back at that moment I want to kill myself.

How to lose your self-respect

Being asked out by a hot girl is always a great boost to your confidence. However, when her asking you out is followed by her telling you to keep it under covers, it breaks your bubble instantly. According to me, there are two reasons as to why a girl would want to keep the fact that she is dating someone a secret. First, she is embarrassed to be seen in public with the guy. Second, she has been in and out of too many relationships and doesn't want people to think she jumps from one relationship to the other. With Shilpa, it was the second case. I believed maybe there was a certain fear of being single for some reason, and so as soon as one ended she would jump into another one. Also, this time she did not want Mr. Palindrome to know because not only was he short and fat and suffered from ED, he was also psychotic. As a guy, the first thing you want to do when you start seeing a hot girl is call all your friends, and people who have always dissed you in life and say, " Guess whom I am dating bitch!" But I had to suppress those feelings and just tell a couple of really close friends, with her permission of course.

Shilpa had asked me out just 4 days before my 22nd birthday. Good-looking women are usually spoilt by guys around her, and this was the case with her too. She was used to going out to nice bars and clubs while I was used to going to shady bars with my friends. But this birthday, I had to take her to a nice place. In India, the birthday boy/girl is supposed to treat his/her friends, which is the complete opposite of the US where the friends treat the person whose birthday it is, which makes so much more sense. I always knew I was made for the US.

Anyway, Shilpa suggested Zenzei, a new upscale lounge in Bandra. I took money from my folks and waited outside the coveted bar for Shilpa. She arrived shortly wearing a poncho. For those who don't really keep up with fashion, poncho is a garment which is usually made of wool to keep you warm, or if it is made of light material, to keep you dry in the rain. But here she was in the middle on the Mumbai summer wearing a poncho. I thought it was a ridiculous piece of clothing but obviously I was not going to comment on her clothes on our first date. Inside, she called for a screwdriver while I called for my standard Old Monk rum and coke. My drink was for Rs. 500! A whole bottle of Old Monk was worth Rs. 250. I had a budget of 2 grand for the night so I quickly made a beeline for the exit citing a reason that the SNFT clan was waiting for us. I was supposed to meet them later in the night to be honest, but I had to expedite the plans a bit so that Shilpa didn't think I was a cheapskate. We all got drunk and suddenly Shilpa had to pee. We were in the middle of nowhere, with no restaurant or anything resembling a restroom close to miles. So she decided to take a leak in the bushes. Now I am sure many of you women have done that, and men do it all the time, but how many of you women have had to do that when you are too drunk to sit down? If I let Shilpa do it all by herself, she would have fallen for sure. So, being a gentleman again, I held her hand and looked away while she was sitting. This first date was proving to be more memorable than I could have ever imagined it to be. As I was driving her back home, in her drunken stupor, Shilpa asked me to stop the car somewhere so we could have some "alone time". I might have been a gentleman before, but no way in hell was I going to give up an opportunity like that. Many of you might be thinking what a jerk I am to take advantage of an inebriated girl. To shed some light on why I am the way I am when it comes to women, I will have to deviate a bit here to tell you a bit about the colony I grew up in.

The Reserve Bank of India colony (Santacruz) comprised of two sub-colonies, both on either side of a street. One was the staff quarters while the other the officers' quarters. My family lived in the staff quarters at first and then moved to the officers' quarters once my dad got promoted. Being a colony, there were a lot of guys to play with, and a lot of girls to letch at. Most of the guys I knew, and grew up with, were just born horny I suppose. The only thing we would do apart from playing cricket or football would be looking at girls. Some of them were so screwed up in the head that all they could think of even during a beautiful and fun festival like *Holi* was to touch women inappropriately while trying to put some color on them. There was even a point of time where all the guys would gather at one person's house to watch porn every afternoon. After watching it in the group, if it was good, everyone would get turns to watch the DVD alone, for obvious reasons. Amongst these guys who had all this pent up sexual urges, I was one of the very few who would actually be meeting real women to put it nicely. So you can imagine the pressure on me to make out on a regular basis and boast about it. Let me be very clear, if I was seriously dating someone, I never ever divulged the details because that is just wrong. But if I was just messing around with some girl, then the guys in my colony would know exactly what happened the next day itself. We had some very interesting people in the colony too. There was a guy who grew the nail on his pinkie finger so he could "finger" a girl well. Another one who got pissed off at his dad once and told him, "Just wait till you become old, I will put you in an old age home!" I grew up with these guys. Can you blame me for turning out the way I did?*

Coming back to the night of my birthday, I pulled over to what I thought was a secluded spot. We moved to the back of my trusty Maruti 800 and what followed will always be a secret my friends. A gentleman never kisses and tells. So even if he goes beyond kissing, the details would never come out. I dropped Shilpa back home and then the following month was just studying for GRE at my place. You can imagine how much we "studied" considering we would be alone at home. The disturbing part was that, at times, my folks would be in the other room.

Soon it was July and Mumbai got one of the worst floods it had ever gotten in a very long time. Shilpa and I were sitting at my place, studying for a change. Soon it started raining heavily. Apparently, the rain-drops hitting her face through the open window were an aphrodisiac for Shilpa. So we engaged in some unholy activities. Within no time however, the water began to rise. I had parked my car outside the colony, and saw that the water had reached up to the doors. Shilpa got a call from her mother who wanted her to be at home as

*Apart from these troubling memories of RBI colony, I even have some sweet ones. Some of my closest friends are from that place.

soon as possible because the situation was only going to get worse with the rain showing no signs of ceasing. Usually when I had to drop Shilpa home, I used to wear a t-shirt and my boxers. My theory was that if I don't have to step out of the car, why bother wearing shorts or pants? That day I stuck to my theory, and went down in similar attire. While I was entering my car, a woman with two young kids whom I assumed she had just picked up from school approached me and asked if she could get a ride with me as her car was not moving in the water. I was more than happy to oblige, and she got in with her kids in the back. My car started but soon I realized that there was too much water for it to even move, and as fast as it had started, my trusty car stalled. I am no parent, and someday I might not even be the best parent around, but this woman in the back of my car started crying rivers because my car had stalled too. When you have your kids with you, how in the world can you be so scared? They are looking for you to tell them that everything will be fine, and you are showing them you are helpless? I understand the situation was scary, but even if you are afraid, don't show it to your kids. The poor kids were really frightened, and started crying too. I felt like punching the woman in the face and taking her kids safely back to their home but sense prevailed and I restrained myself from doing that. I offered to walk her and her kids home, which might have been about a 45 min walk through the water. But she refused and kept looking for other cars. I wish I had just punched her.

So Shilpa and I set off on a long walk back to her place, through waist high water at some places, and me in my boxers and a sleeveless t-shirt. The roads were chaotic to say the least.

Many vehicles were abandoned in the middle of the roads, while some others that were still running were trying to maneuver their way through the array of dead cars. And to add to all the commotion, there were thousands of people on the road trying to get back to the security of their homes by foot. Some of the people, like us, were making the most of it and having some fun. Though I was enjoying the walk back home with Shilpa, walking in wet boxers with the wind blowing wasn't the most comfortable situation around. Let's just say I am glad I did not get dirty thoughts in my head at that moment. After wading through the water for almost a couple of hours, we finally reached Shilpa's house. Her mother was really sweet and also very fond of me if I may add, and she asked me to take a shower while she got me spare clothes. So I was at my girlfriend's house, with her mom serving me amazing hot chocolate, while I was going commando in her dad's clothes. I had never felt so uncomfortable in my life. That was the day I took a stance against me stepping out of the house in my underwear. I always enjoyed hanging out at Shilpa's house. Her family loved me, and they had a great dog named Duster. After I spent the night on her couch, her mom made me breakfast and I was soon walking back through the water to get back home. I reached home for my parents to tell me their story. Apparently, my mom was stuck in a train, and my dad walked all the way from his office, which is in Churchgate, to where the train was stuck in Jogeshwari. To travel that distance by train, it would take at least half-an-hour minimum. So you can imagine how much time it must have taken by foot to cover that much ground. And the smart guy that my father is, he walked all the way to Jogeshwari on the train tracks as there were no trains running anyway. I still believe that it is one of the most romantic things I have ever heard in my life. I really wish someday I will find someone whom I will love as much as my parents love each other.

Remember the list of things I had made that I would never do? I had already had drinks outside my house. Next was the turn of going to clubs. I was never into it but Shilpa loved going out, especially to clubs. So I had to sacrifice my second never-to-do thing, and went to a club with a few of her friends. We went to this place called Bed Lounge in Bandra. It was not as bad as I expected a club to be, but the only problem was that you are allowed to smoke inside bars and clubs in India. Not only it is suffocating, you smell like smoke when you get out. I enjoy smoking too when I am drinking, but I would not want to bother others by it. Another thing about Indian clubs is that people come in groups, and dance around in circles. So when you look at the dance floor from a top view, it will look like the Olympics symbol, with non-interlocking circles. A circle was never to be broken. In a club, there will obviously be guys who are there to hook up with women. But if they try to break a circle, the guys in that circle would try to break them. It is just ridiculous because the women want to be hit on too, but the guys are retards who think they are responsible for all the women they have come with. All in all, I enjoyed my first time in a club watching these funny people and dancing with my hot girlfriend. So we started going out to clubs more often. One day, a friend of Shilpa's, Roma, whom I always found very attractive, decided to join us. As we started dancing, Shilpa started dancing with this very good guy friend of hers. So I started dancing with Roma. Now what transpired was something really unexpected. Roma and I started dancing really close. As a matter of fact, soon we were grinding like crazy. I was turned on and I am pretty damn sure she was too. It was not at all my intention for it to happen, but it just did. But nothing else happened, and soon we left to get home before our curfew. Next day, Shilpa starts telling me how cheap it was for me to do that. I completely understood what she was saying and I apologized for it too. But the thing about women is they can keep nagging you about the same thing for ages. The scene in Jerry Maguire, where Renee Zellweger says, "You had me at hello", is something that will never ever happen. That scene gives all men hope. Hope that we might not have to keep apologizing till the end of time; that our better half will understand our plight of being a less evolved species and just forgive us. But it never happens. And the same was the case with Shilpa too. She kept nagging me about it. I knew I was at fault and kept apologizing. Then she tells me something that just stopped my heart for a minute. She told me that while I was dancing with Roma, she called Mr. Palindrome up to tell him what I was up to and that she was pissed off at me. What was I to make out of that? She had just called her ex-boyfriend when she was pissed off with me. It really hurt me but I decided not to throw any tantrums as I was at fault too.

After being with Shilpa for 2 months, things were looking good. One fine day, we were sitting at home as usual studying for our GRE exams, which we were to TAKE in September, when she gets a call from Mr. Palindrome. The annoying part was that this guy had been blackmailing Shilpa with some explicit pictures he had of her. Shilpa was stupid enough to send him some of those pictures when they were trying to work the long distance relationship. But this guy was such a loser, that he was now blackmailing her with these photos and also threatening to ruin her life if she did not stop seeing me. As a matter of fact, he even told her once that he would make sure life would be miserable for Shilpa and I, no matter which university we attended in the US because he had friends everywhere. On a scale of 1 to 10 for sore losers, this guy was definitely a 100. And Shilpa was actually answering this douchebag's calls. She continued to talk to him for an hour sitting at my house. Then I decided to drop her home as I was really getting too pissed off. While I was chauffeuring her, she was still on the phone with that guy; laughing at times, crying some times. I could not understand the range of emotions I was seeing from Shilpa, especially when talking to a guy who was downright blackmailing her. As we were near her place, she hung up the phone. I honestly asked her if she was over Mr. Palindrome, to which she said she wasn't but still she wanted to be with me. I dropped her, and as I was about to leave, she asks me," Aren't you going to kiss me?" What I really wanted to do was yell at the top of my voice, but what I did was kissed her and went home. And that my friends, is how you lose MOST of your self-respect.

After finishing up with my GRE, and applying to schools, I had started working for an internet solutions company that provided web hosting and domain services. It was a completely different field for me considering I was a production engineer and I was in the sales and marketing division of this company. But it was a good experience as I got to talk to a lot of customers first hand, and understand marketing strategies as well. I met some great people there and it was a lot of fun as the whole company had a very young and carefree environment.

More importantly, it paid me Rs.15,000 a month which would make sure I could keep my high maintenance girlfriend happy. I have no idea how but I would finish up all my salary for a month within the first couple of weeks itself. There was a time when I could have lived like a king with Rs.2000 for a month. And now I had almost 8 times that amount, but had to borrow money from my folks by mid month. One day after I got my salary, as usual I decided to go out with Shilpa to a nice place called Rio near the Seven Bungalows area. We were to be joined there by Vanita, Vanita's friend Nina, and a few of my friends from the football team. The place had a very different setting to it. There were mattresses on the floor, next to the wall so that we could sit on the mattresses, with the walls acting as lumbar support. We sat there for a while and had a few drinks till all of us were buzzed. I was sitting between Vanita and Nina, while Shilpa sat next to Vanita and the football team guys next to Shilpa one after the other. Vanita started to say something to Nina, but being a bit drunk Nina said, "Look I am not listening to a word you are saying, I am just staring at your boobs!" I found this hilarious. I never thought this Nina girl was funny as such but after that statement I had newfound respect for this woman. And to go with the flow, I followed suit by saying, "Me too! Me too!" Apparently, this did not sit well with Vanita who thought I was actually staring at her breasts or something; self-obsessed people these women are I tell you. So she starts nagging Shilpa about how I said something like that and that she should do something about it. Shilpa ignored it at first but Vanita was persistent and kept at it till Shilpa got really pissed off. Now I can understand my girlfriend getting pissed off if I made a statement like that seriously. But this was totally different because I was just messing around and she did not even know in what context I said it. But Shilpa was pissed. So what does she do instead of talking to me privately? She slaps me as hard as possible, in front of my teammates. I had no idea what had happened for a second. I didn't even realize I had been slapped. But this was the limit. How could a girl treat me like that? So I did what every self-respecting man would do. I took her to my car, made her do me a "favor" and then dropped her home. And that my friends, is how you lose ALL your self-respect.

Though we had a few rough times, Shilpa and I were going strong, thanks primarily to my aforementioned lack of self-respect. We always had a great time together and we could just be friends most of the time which is always important according to me in a relationship. Furthermore, both our families knew about it too and were happy about it too. I would spend a lot of time with her family. They had a house in Pune which they would visit often as Shilpa's sister was studying in Pune and lived there. During their visits, I would mostly be the designated driver who would drive them from Mumbai to Pune and back. The drive is a 4-hour journey, so pretty much like the drive between Boston and New York *sans* the beautiful scenery or the New York skyline. So you have to understand, it was a big effort on my part to actually make that trip few times. But the thing was I actually enjoyed it. I got to spend time with Shilpa, and I got to spend time with her mom whom I really adored. I treated her like a friend where I could make fun of her and talk to her about anything and she would be cool about it. Even her dad really liked me. So much so, that once their whole family had gone to South India for a nice vacation for a few weeks. They could not take Duster along so I volunteered to stay at their place and take care of him for the weeks they were to be away. Shilpa's dad made sure I would have all my needs taken care of, including telling me that I could invite my friends over and have a few drinks if I wanted to. He even showed me where he kept his bottle of whiskey! I did misunderstand him a bit when he said a few drinks because by the end of it we had finished his bottles and he literally was offering us only a few drinks. I still owe him a bottle of Black Label.

My parents were getting jealous of the fact that I was spending so much time with her parents as opposed to them. I thought it was really cute but the way my mom put it, it was anything but. It was like a dialogue straight out of Marie's mouth in 'Everybody Loves Raymond'. My mom tells me, "So now her family is more important to you than us huh? You love them more than us don't you?" Again, I blame the Indian cinema for this family drama. Every movie you watch has to have family drama in it. Doesn't matter if it is a horror movie or a funny movie, family drama is a must. What was my response to my mom's statement? I replied, "Mom, I am going to Goa for New Years."

Goa is a famous tourist spot in India. Goa is a place where half of India, and most of Mumbai, ends up for New

Year celebrations every year. I had never been there, unlike most of the people I was going with, and was really excited about going there. I was going with the SNFT clan, Shilpa, and a school friend of Shilpa's. There were a lot of rumors of how Goa is the cheapest place for booze, but let me just clarify that myth right here that Goa is only cheap if you go there during times when there will be absolutely no tourists. New Year time is when they have the most tourists, and also the time when the place is as expensive as hell. We hired a few bikes, one without gears which I got as I did not have a bike license. We set out at night to go to a beach about 20 minutes away. It was a bit chilly with the wind blowing into our faces. So I came up with the theory that if I was to ride faster, I would get there sooner and hence less time in the cold breeze. This theory could also be called the 'How to Get Yourself Killed' theory. I completely forgot one very important thing about India; the roads suck! As I was on the bike at close to its highest speed, with Shilpa riding pillion, the bike hit a small pothole which was enough for me to lose my balance. The bike toppled over, throwing both of us off onto the shoulder luckily. I got up to see that my arm was bruised and bleeding a bit. To lessen the embarrassment, I chose to sit down holding my hand, pretending to be really hurt. Shilpa walked up to me, looked at my hand, then just lifted her skirt to her knees and showed me how badly she was injured which was way worse, and just walked away. That was the last time I ever whined on that trip. Most of the next day was spent on a beach, relaxing, having beer, getting fake tattoos. At night we decided to go to this really small restaurant called Asterix. And when I say small, it was really small with just 4 tables, and a very limited menu. It was a family run business, with the man, his wife, and their good-looking daughter. They had a guy playing the guitar and singing, and he was just amazing. We sat there for a few hours, had a lot of drinks, with one of my friends trying to hit on the good-looking hostess. We had a German group sitting there too, and one of the guys volunteered to sing and he was just brilliant. It is absolutely amazing where in the world you might find astounding talent. By this time, we were all pretty hammered and Shilpa decided to make an announcement. She held my hand, stood up, and told everyone there, "We are going back to the hotel. Give us half-an-hour at least." This was followed by laughter, and a remark by an English guy who said, "Now we know who has the balls in the relationship." After our little adventure in the room, we both fell asleep. We completely forgot that we were to share the room with 2 others. As a result, 6 people had to somehow sleep on a double bed, with one of the guys throwing up in the middle of the night. Good times.

After the Goa trip, Shilpa was busy with her final exams and me at work. After getting done with her exams, it was time for us to start shopping for our travel to the land of opportunities in summer. One day we went shopping with a couple of Shilpa's close friends, one of whom was Alice or Allie as she was called. Allie was a decent looking girl with a good body. But obviously after the incident with Roma at the club, I was not even going to look at any of Shilpa's friends. That night when Shilpa and I were fooling around, she started talking dirty and asked me to name a girl I would like to have a threesome with. Now let me tell all you guys out there, never

ever answer that question. And if you do, make sure you name some celebrity. After being around Allie all day, hers was the name that first popped in my head and that came out of my mouth. Shilpa didn't say anything then and went along with the dirty talk. Come next day, and the nagging slowly started. I just pretended I was not listening to her. For some reason, Allie started spreading rumors that I was hitting on her. As a matter of fact, she told someone that I told her that I wanted to have sex with her. The timing could not have been worse considering that Shilpa was nagging me about the same woman. One thing led to another and soon there was a big fight between Shilpa and Allie on the phone. Though Shilpa had doubts about it, she totally believed in me and took a stand. To clear the thing out, they decided to meet at a coffee shop. Why in the world would you want to meet at a public place when you know there is going to be a lot of drama? The meeting at the coffee shop was insane. Allie's side got witnesses, which was all hearsay if I may add, and we had some friends too. It was a battle royale, with both sides yelling, except me because I was too embarrassed because everyone at the coffee shop was staring at us. We just left the matter unresolved, as there was inconclusive evidence on both sides. Just to set the record straight, I did not do anything with Allie; well at least not at that point in my life.

Soon it was our last few months in Mumbai. I was more than happy to get out of Mumbai. Of course, all the reasons I am going to mention now are my opinion. So all of you can have your own opinions too. I know there are a lot of people who love that city, and think it is the place to be in India. There is always a constant debate too as to which city is better,

Mumbai or Delhi. Well, here is a newsflash my fellow Indians, both cities are annoying. Don't get me wrong here; I do not mind visiting Mumbai. After all, I was born and raised there, have my family and friends there, and a lot of memories. But what is so great about the city? Is it the slums that have popped up everywhere that are a great sight? Or the insane traffic which makes a 10 minute drive to last 45 minutes minimum? Driving rules are not at all followed in the city because everyone knows that you can get away with bribing the traffic police. If you are waiting at a red light, people behind you start honking 10-15 seconds before the signal is to go green. Where do you want me to go??? Public transport is something that the Mumbaiyyas are happy about. The trains are so overcrowded that people hang outside doors and windows to make to work on time. Hundreds of people die falling off the train, or get electrocuted by travelling on top of the trains. And of course, the overcrowded trains not only provide a great hunting ground for pickpockets, but also molesters. During my undergraduate years, I was travelling via train to make a football game on time. I was wearing shorts considering I was running late and did not want to change at the ground. While standing in the crazily crowded train, I felt someone's hand grazing my crotch. Being so crowded, I could not move, and also decided to give the guy the benefit of the doubt. After many stops, there was more than enough room for everyone to stand without being within 2 feet of each other. But this guy still had his hand on my junk. If you saw this guy, you would never imagine him to be a pervert. He was a well-dressed, middle-aged man, carrying a swanky leather briefcase. I moved away, but within a few stops this guy was again touching me. I was about to tell him off when he decided to get off the train. I think a lot of these sexual encounters with gay men have to do with the fact that India is still not open about gays. Gays are still treated in India like how African-Americans were treated in the US back in the day.

Apart from the traffic, the pollution, the molestation and the overcrowded city, one thing that the Mumbaiyyas love is that the city never sleeps. There is always a hustle and bustle about it. Many have told me that it is so great that we can buy alcohol at 4am if needed. Would that really be a reason to love the city? I have done it too but what is so great in the availability of alcohol that late into the night? It is just one more reason for people to drink and drive.

Political issues are another major issue when it comes to Mumbai. If you are not politically correct, you will be beat up. There is nothing such as your opinion, it is the opinion of the leaders that you must follow. If you participate in Valentine's Day celebrations, you are bound to be beat up. There have been incidents where women were dragged out of parties, and stripped naked for enjoying this day. If someone were to mention Mumbai with its old name, Bombay, they are made to publically apologize. Politicians should have their opinion and that's their right. But it is also their right for people to do and say as per their choice. However, the concept of democracy is somewhat lost in the city. Many of you will argue that I am only talking about the underbelly of the city here, and that there are positives too which I most definitely agree to. Unfortunately, the underbelly is a bit too overpowering for the positives to really shine through.

Now let me talk a bit about Delhi. I have personally never been to Delhi so I won't be able to talk about it as much as I have about Mumbai. But I know a lot of people from the capital, and their views and beliefs of the city. Also, I unfortunately have a tendency to read some news once in a while, and the news that one will always see in an Indian newspaper is about a rape in Delhi. Here are some figures to give you an idea of the crime rate in our great national capital. Delhi reported over 30.5 percent, 406 out of the total 1,329 rape cases in a survey of 35 mega cities across the country in 2003*. For kidnapping and abduction of women, Delhi counted for 35 percent (673) of the total 1,921 cases. In the same year, Delhi reported a 793 percent increase in cases of cruelty by husbands and relatives. Among the big cities, Delhi tops the crime graph with an average rate of 328.1 as against 156.9, 81.1 and 133.5 for Mumbai, Kolkata and Chennai. According to a recent survey, 96% of women in Delhi felt unsafe. Apart from this, when you talk to a person from South Delhi, you will see this attitude in them for being from that region. I do understand that South Delhi is where all the rich people live but kids why would you want to act like jerks just because your parents are rich? If you earn that much and then decide to throw around some attitude, be my guest! Also, the Delhi metro is something every Delhiite is proud of, and something they love to boast about. I do admit it looks great, and it is something the nation should be proud of as a whole. But again when you compare the Delhi metro to the subway systems all across the world, it would hardly feature in the top 10. Many might argue as to why we should compare something

*Google didn't provide me with more recent numbers.

in India to anything outside the country. I say why not? If we are to be considered a developed country, should we not compare ourselves with others to see where we stand? A diehard Shah Rukh Khan fan once asked me, "Why the hell are you comparing Shah Rukh to American actors? It does not make sense." This was coming from a guy who had compared education at a masters level in India to that in the US, and had decided to move here. Of course, a lot of them decide to do masters in the US so that they get better *dowry* when they get married. But in the end, you are comparing. If you can compare one thing, you can, and should, compare everything. Coming back to Delhi, there are a lot of historic sites and places there which are definitely something to look forward to visit. However, would you really want to live amongst criminals, perverts, and pompous jackasses? So which city would you prefer out of the two? I guess it is in the end a question of the lesser of two evils. If I were to make a choice, I pick.....Cochin, Kerala.

Shilpa and I were into our final few weeks in Mumbai. We had both been accepted into Northeastern University (NU) in Boston. I had even been accepted in University of Southern California (USC) which is a very high ranked school compared to NU. However, Shilpa failed to get into USC which was surprising as everyone who applied there would get in. I decided not to go to a higher ranked school, and go to NU to be with my girlfriend. That was one of the stupidest things I have done in my life. Please, to all you future PIGS out there, select schools based on their rankings and how good your program is there; not on your current or prospective partners.

Shilpa and I also decided to move in together, which was a big decision, but it seemed like the right thing to do and it seemed like we were ready for it too. But we needed roommates and did not know anyone. So we attended a meeting of all the students going to NU from Mumbai. Everyone met up in Bandra to discuss what was to be done before travelling and what is to be carried with you. We were looking for a couple of girls who would be willing to share a 2-bedroom apartment, and be okay with a guy in the house. We found a girl, Divya, who was willing to live with us and was looking for girl to share her room with.

I was going from one hellhole to the other. The day we had to leave, there was frantic packing going on with my dad going crazy over the weight of bags I was to carry. Even if we had gone over by a few kilos, it would not have been a big deal as Shilpa's dad had already pulled a few strings and told some of the officials at the airport that we were to travel that night. Just before I was to leave for the airport, I got a call from Vedika wishing me luck. She even started crying reminiscing about the past, saying how things had gone in a completely different direction from what we had hoped it would at one point in our lives. She meant all of it as a friend, and it was something really sweet, and something that I will always remember. Soon we were at the airport, with the whole SNFT clan and Vanita there to send us off, apart from both our families of course. This was the first time our families were to meet. And to my relief, they were really friendly and got along well. After saying our goodbyes to our friends, we went in with our families to check in our bags. As the officials knew Shilpa's father, both our families were allowed to come with us up till the security clearance. As we started saying our goodbyes to our parents, my mom burst out into tears. For some reason, I never thought my mother would be sad to see me go. I always figured that once I left, my folks would get fewer complaints about our house being a brothel of some sort. But still my mom cried and it felt nice. I'm not being sadistic here, just that it was emotional. I said my goodbyes to Shilpa's parents and soon we were boarding the plane which would fly us to the land of dreams; well actually the plane which would fly us to Frankfurt, Germany and then the final flight from Frankfurt which would take us to the land of dreams.

Anecdote : My to-do list

The following is the list of things I would like to do before I am buried.

1. Earn copious amounts of money.
2. Buy some great cars.
3. Join the mile high club.
4. Asian.
5. Actress.

The last 2 are not things but people, but you get the drift.

When in Rome, do as the Romans do.
When in the US, act like a fob

The flight from Mumbai to Frankfurt was a bit tough to sit in for a 6'1" tall guy like me. With barely any leg space, you can imagine how amazingly comfortable it was for the entire 8-hour duration of the flight. However, the wine definitely helped. I think that is the main purpose of providing free liquor on international flights; people get drunk and forget their inconveniences and later when asked how their flight was, they would just describe it was wonderful. I was 4 wine glasses down and that is more than enough on a flight. And I was enjoying the in-flight movie Taxi No. 9211, the Bollywood movie "inspired" by the Ben Affleck, Samuel L. Jackson starrer Changing Lanes. I really like how Indian directors draw "inspiration" from pretty much every Hollywood movie, apart from of course the Indian family dramas which can really be scripted by any Tom, Dick or Harry. Recently, a big Hollywood studio sued an Indian studio for copying a certain movie. If only Hollywood knew how many movies were actually copied, without even changing a single scene. Anyway, coming back to Taxi No. 9211, watching Sameera Reddy, the heroine, was turning me on a bit. She might not be the best looking actress in tinsel town, but she is tall, dusky, and has a good body. To add to the effect, she was wet in one of the songs, and I was drunk. So I started nudging Shilpa who was fast asleep by then. This was a great opportunity for us to join the mile high club, one thing to strike off from the list. But Shilpa just could not be persuaded into it. Maybe I should have just gone into the restroom and helped myself. Does that count towards membership of the club?

After the stopover at Frankfurt, the flight to Boston was way better with a lot of leg space. However, to spoil the comfort, they were showing a movie on cheerleaders. We landed in Boston around noon. After the immigration clearance, we met Neil, a family friend of Shilpa's who was supposed to help us get to the place where we were going to live temporarily. Usually, new students live in temporary accommodation provided by the Indian Student association where the new people are put in with some seniors till they can find accommodation of their own. This was a great thing for the seniors to do, and a good way for the newcomers to settle down. However, due to the large number of Indian students coming in every year, they had to accommodate around 10-15 people in one house. So you can imagine the chaos in a 2-bedroom house with 15 people, and 3 large suitcases per person that they got from India. Some seniors would graciously offer to cook food as well, but would charge the new people some minimal amount which completely made sense. However, the problem with us Indians is that if we pay for something, we make sure that we utilize it to the fullest. I have heard stories of some guys eating half a box of cereal for breakfast, no exaggeration here, because they had paid money for food so might as well make the most of it. Considering all this, we decided not to live in the temporary accommodation provided by Sanskriti, the Indian Students association at Northeastern University, and made our arrangements with Megha, a girl from Rehan's class in undergrad whom I knew well. Actually, I knew her well because Rehan and I used to make a lot of fun of her, in a friendly way of course but still to a point where it was just downright mean. She was nice enough to forget all that, and let us live with her. The cab ride from the airport to Megha's place cost us around $50, and Neil asked us to tip him a further $10. The tip concept was again something very new to us. In India, you take a rickshaw or a cab, pay the driver and actually wait for him to give back every single rupee. Here, on the other hand, the cab driver waits for you to give him more than the meter. So we ended up paying $60 for the cab, which we quickly converted into Rupees and realized that we had got a Rs. 3000 setback already. The land of opportunities suddenly seemed like the land that wanted to take away our money.

Shilpa and I had come to Boston a good couple of months before school were to start. This gave us enough time to look for apartments, get through whatever formalities we could before orientation, and also find an on-campus job which was the most important for any graduate student as it paid for your food and rent. At NU, the highest paying job was the Residential Security Office (RSO) and as we were one of the very few already there for the next semester, it was easy for us to get a job there. Finding an apartment was way tougher. Going to different realtors, who take you to a dozen houses every day, is a tiring process. But finally we found a nice apartment within our budget. We could not finalize it as yet as we had to wait for Divya, our roommate from Mumbai, to come take a look too. After Divya arrived, and we finalized the same apartment, Shilpa and I had nothing left to do at school so we decided to visit everyone we knew. First on the list was Namrata, a high school friend of Shilpa's who had been in the US for quite some time, and was living in New York. So we took the cheap Chinatown bus to New York. New York, or the Big Apple as it is known; a city that literally never sleeps. No matter what the time is, you will find something to do in NY. The subway system is running 24/7 which makes sure you are never stranded anywhere. Times Square, a block that is so lit up with billboards day and night that you will always find people with their mouth agape at any given time of the day at Times Square. These are some things that people who love NY would say. Now here is my take on NY. According to me, New York is a blown up version of Mumbai. If I didn't like the smaller version, why in the world would I like the bigger one? There are hundreds and thousands of people in your face all the time. NY drivers are as bad as Mumbai, with honking and changing lanes as prominent and frequent as its Indian counterpart. I do understand that you will always find something to do in NY, no matter what the time but if you are looking for something to do after 4-5am, there is something seriously wrong with you. There is something that people usually do at night after a certain time. It is this really nice thing that calms you and relaxes you. I believe it is called sleep. Cleanliness also does not seem to be a priority in the Big Apple for some reason. New Yorkers are proud of the so-called New York Pizza, a ridiculously large pizza, which is way overpriced. NY does have some nice places to visit like the MET, the Guggenheim, Central Park, Rockefeller Centre, and many more. But then again which city doesn't have some landmarks?

Namrata took us around NY and one of the things I was introduced to the first day there was bagels and cream cheese. This is staple breakfast for a lot of people in the US. With cream cheese containing 34g of fat for every 100g, it isn't too hard to figure out why America has the highest rate of obesity in the world when you also throw in all the possible fast food chains you can fathom the picture. The whole day was spent in roaming around the city. Come night time, and it was time to party. As usual, I decided to pre-game before going out. This would help a lot financially as well. So we bought a bottle of cheap white wine, and as I got dressed way earlier than the women, I started having the wine straight out of the bottle. And before I knew it, the bottle was finished with Shilpa and Namrata having a couple of sips from it. We were soon joined by Namrata's boyfriend and left for the club called The Park. We arrived there and started off with shots, followed by a couple of drinks. By the time we hit the dance floor on the upper level, I was completely hammered. Suddenly, I see a white guy stand up on one of the tables next to the dance floor and pull down his pants. I was more than impressed by this move as everyone on the dance floor was looking at him and applauding the obscenity. Being the attention whore, I wanted to emulate him and so I stood up on the table and yelled that I was going to drop my pants too. Apparently, a brown kid dropping his pants is not really a head turner. To add to the embarrassment, standing on the table was enough to make me want to vomit. So I jumped down and started running downstairs where the restroom was. But I could not control it, and puke started coming out. I left a nice little trail for everyone from the top of the stairs to the restroom so that anyone who was concerned about me would be able to find me with ease. No one was concerned, including my girlfriend, was a different issue all together.

The next morning, with a nice hangover, we bid adieu to Namrata and left for New Jersey where we were to stay with Shilpa's aunt. I was excited to visit New Jersey as it is known as the armpit of America. However, much to my disappointment, her aunt lived in a very upscale neighborhood of NJ, in Princeton. They had a beautiful house, with two great kids who were a lot of fun too. Shilpa's aunt's husband was an amazing guy too, who grilled some stake, got out some nice Robert Mondavi to go along with it. It was a perfect getaway, and I saw them living the great American dream, something I wanted. After living with them for a couple of days, we left for Boston reluctantly. However, I had one last trip planned before school started, and that was to visit my brother in Boulder, Colorado.

When the flight takes off at Boston Logan International Airport, all you see are the buildings and the Boston harbor. When the flight descends to land at Denver International Airport, all you see are the breath taking Rocky Mountains which stretch for miles and miles. This first sight of Colorado was enough for me to fall in love with the place. At that time, i.e. in 2006, my brother had only one German Shepherd, Jaeger*, who was not even a year old then. Now he has two, the second being Iris. Both are now over 3 years old and weigh around 100 pounds; so basically they are big dogs. Let me take this opportunity to tell you a bit about my brother and his relationship with his dogs. My brother Ashish is a single guy

*Contrary to popular belief, Jaeger was not named after Jagermeister. Jaeger means Hunter in German.

who has been working for the past 5 years now. He first got Jaeger so that he has some company, and then got Iris so that Jaeger has some company. If you think that Paris Hilton's little Chihuahua* might be the most spoilt dog on the planet, wait till you meet these brats. They refuse to acknowledge you when you try to give them treats if those treats have no meat in them. Milkbones and dog biscuits have no place in his house. Both of dogs have their own disadvantages. Jaeger is more accommodating towards other dogs and loves playing with them. On the other hand, Iris, being the bitch that she is (literally), barks at everything that moves. However, if you are playing with them with toys, it is pretty much impossible to get something back from Jaeger once he has it in his mouth. We have even tried to pry his mouth open but to no avail. Iris will give you the toy at the drop of a hat. Now here comes the funny part. You know how you call someone lovey-dovey names; be it your partner or your kids? Well, my brother calls them names too but mostly based on what is coming on the television at that time. Some of the names I have heard him call them are Little Benjamin Button, Little Advil and the Biggie Advil, Little Matrix, Biggie Cheesecake and so on and so forth. When in Colorado, camping is one of the activities I love doing. The drive to and from the camping grounds is usually beautiful. However, as you are high up in the mountains for camping, the drive back is downhill and if you are the passenger with my brother, it is a bit hard to enjoy the drive. You see my brother doesn't really believe in the speed limit signs put up for the sharp turns. He always goes at least

*One of my FOB (Fresh of the boat) friends once pronounced Chihuahua as Chi-hu-hu-ha-ha. At first I thought it was his evil laughter, only to realize he was in fact talking about the species of dogs.

10mph faster than the speed limit on the sharp turns which results in the centrifugal force pushing your face almost up against the window. And while he is doing this, if the any one of the dogs are awake in the back of the car and not sleeping, he will start talking to them by looking at the rear-view mirror. Now don't get me wrong but I love Jaeger and Iris to death, and if I were asked to choose between their life and mine, I would choose theirs. But plunging to my death from around 1000 feet is not exactly how I would like to sacrifice myself for them. I would choose a more subtle way; maybe dying of age could be my way to go.

Back to 2006, and I thoroughly enjoyed my three weeks in Boulder. Played with Jaeger the whole day, had a drink and watched movies with my brother at night. We even went camping to this place called Salida where we put up a tent right next to a river with the door of the tent facing the river and the back of the tent facing the mountain range. It was my first camping trip and it was too much fun. After 3 weeks, while I was on my flight back to Boston, I realized one thing; I would be perfectly happy with being a husband who sits at home and takes cares of the kids and the dogs while my wife works her ass off to put food on the table. Women have been crying about equal opportunities all their life and I just want to give them that equal opportunity while I get the opportunity to take care of the kids.

A couple of weeks before school were to start, we moved in to our new apartment. Divya had found a roommate from Delhi whom everyone liked to call Doggy based on her email address which had doggy in it. Shilpa and I set up our room and by the end of it, the room was as girly as it could get. So in order to prove that a guy lived in that room, I went out and got a Pink Floyd poster, the one where all the women are sitting by the pool, naked with their backs towards the camera and each woman's back is painted to represent a Floyd album. And that particular 55 x 40 inch piece of wall was my manly domain, all mine. Soon it was time for our orientation where we would meet the other international students that had come in that year to Northeastern. To our surprise, the room was filled with hundreds of Indians. I had come from India, to mini India. Shilpa was wearing a summer dress which was knee length, and as a result, had all the Gujjus straight out of the state of Gujarat staring at her legs. They were staring so hard that I was getting embarrassed. After orientation, we could start working on our on-campus jobs and soon it was my first shift, which was to be a graveyard shift from 11pm to 7am. The work was basically to swipe in students into their dormitories, and so usually there would be a lot of free time sitting at one dorm for 8 hours, especially at night. Most of the students buy laptops as soon as they get here. However, I had taken my brother's desktop which he wasn't using, and so I did not need a laptop. In order to keep myself from falling asleep, I carried with myself Erich Segal's Love Story, a book gifted to me by the SNFT group before I left for the US. Within a couple of hours of the shift, the students coming in died down and I started with the book. By 4am, I finished the book with tears in my eyes. Till now you might not have thought of me as someone who might cry reading a book. But I am a romantic by nature, and this book is for all the people like me. I loved it so much that I read it once more before the shift ended!

Classes started soon too and I was to have a tough semester considering I had two very difficult subjects to deal with in Operations Research and Engineering Probability & Statistics. However, for a change, I loved my professors and was actually looking forward to the next class. The first week came with another surprise. Shilpa had got a teaching assistantship (TA). Though that was good news which meant she would only have to pay half of her tuition, I got pissed off when I found out that she was working with a professor who teaches mechanical engineering subjects; my subjects to be more precise. This was a girl who had absolutely no clue about her own subjects, forget the ones from my department. In the following weeks, Shilpa would come to me everyday regarding doubts on the subject she was a TA for. I don't know if she did it on purpose to rub it in my face, or if she was just dumb, but I was definitely getting annoyed. In a month's time, it was mid-terms time. In India, as I have mentioned earlier in the book, I never bothered about mid-terms. However, it did matter a lot to me here. I studied really hard and went for my first mid-term which was to be the Operations Research one. As the professor entered the class with the mid-term papers, some students started booing him. This was a guy who had done masters and PhD from reputed universities in the US, and he was being booed. What does he do? He laughs and apologizes for having to take the tests. For me, those were the coolest words that had ever come out of a professor's mouth. If I were to boo a professor in India, I would most definitely be suspended from school for a couple of weeks, with a chance of being thrown out permanently too if the professor was vindictive enough. When I was applying to schools in the US, I was to take letter of recommendations from some of my professors. One day one of them suddenly started yelling at me because he thought I was not thanking him enough. If your wife is not giving you any, don't take that out on me man; that is what I wanted to say but wisely chose not to.

Being a TA, Shilpa also had to do some lab work, which is where she met Crassy. Crassy was a cool guy, one of the few cool guys I had met at NU. He was an intelligent student, coupled with the fact that he was also into sports, especially racquetball. Racquetball is just like squash, just a bit different. We started playing almost every day, along with a third friend Pramod. After racquetball, we would all go to Crassy's apartment, call for food, and have some beers and head back home. Shilpa would join us too. It pretty much became a ritual. Apart from a few people I knew well, I also put it in my head that I was above every other Indian there. According to me, I looked better, had a hot girlfriend, and had friends to hang out with and drink. What more could you want in life? Also, when one Indian student sees another on the streets, apparently it is an unsaid rule to smile at each other. But I am not the kind of person to smile at people I did not even know. As a matter of fact, sometimes I don't even acknowledge people I have been introduced to. As a result of all the above-mentioned, Indian graduate students labeled me as an asshole with too much attitude. I really didn't care about what people thought about me as long as I had my small circle of people working for me.

I was doing well in my classes and was pretty much on course for an A in both. However, I did manage to screw up my Operations Research final. Apparently, the optional chapter rule which applied in India did not apply here as every chapter was covered in exams. I was disappointed after that final as I knew I had messed up my grade. At that disappointing time, I also left my job at the RSO. Why you ask? Well, they made me. You see as Shilpa had a lot of free time as she did not have to work on campus anymore considering she was getting funding from her TA position, and so she wanted to visit Namrata in NY and her aunt in NJ quite often. And of course, she had to take me along. I missed a lot of my shifts because of that, and in the end left them with no choice. All in all, I was very frustrated with my life at that point. So Shilpa came up with this brilliant plan to cheer me up. Her undergraduate classmates, whom I knew well too, were meeting up in Berkeley at one of the girl's apartments, and so Shilpa wanted to go there too. When she suggested this, I wanted to ask her if she pretended to be dumb, or if she was just born like that. How could I financially manage a trip to California when I had no income whatsoever? But you know how women can get when they want something. She pretended to be sad, and also told me that she would not go without me. I kept telling her I had no money but she told me that I could borrow it from her, and then return it whenever. So finally, I reluctantly agreed to go, with my brother paying for my ticket.

Unable to join the mile high club again, we landed in Oakland after a 5-hour flight. After sitting in the BART, the train service for the Bay Area, we reached the girl's, Donna's place where we were supposed to crash at. The place was way filthier than you would expect a student's house to be. Donna explained that one of her roommates, who was from Delhi, did not believe in clean living habits and as it was her turn to do some cleaning, the house was a mess. I did not know if this was a coincidence, but my roommate Doggy who was also coincidentally from Delhi, did not like to clean things. As a matter of fact, I firmly believed she should have been called Piggy and not Doggy. ~~Piggy~~ Doggy would never help around the house, and whenever she did help after a lot of convincing, she would clean up like an F1 car on a 100m stretch; you blink and it is gone. Also, Doggy had this oh so awesome habit of dumping her used sanitary napkin in the dustbin in the restroom. I don't want blood on a sanitary napkin to be the first thing I see in the morning. As a matter of fact, it is something I never want to see. I secretly used to wish she got laid and subsequently pregnant, but unfortunately I becoming the President of the United States of America had a better chance than her getting laid. As no one wanted to live, even if it was for 5 days, in a filthy apartment, we all decided to give Donna a hand and cleaned up the place in a couple of hours.

Our first day in Berkeley, Donna took us around the Berkeley campus and it was beautiful to say the least. The Berkeley campus looked enormous compared to its Northeastern counterpart, and I was definitely impressed. After walking around all day, we decided to go to a South Indian place for dinner. If I wanted South Indian food, I would have sat at home in India with my mom serving me the best South Indian food possible. I did not fly thousands of miles to

Boston, and then fly to California for the same food. But hey as they say, when in Rome do as the Romans; act stupid. The next day was more exciting. We went to San Francisco and I instantly fell in love with the city. It is a beautiful city with the bay right next to it, and some great seafood places. The first place to visit, however, had to be Alcatraz.

This legendary penitentiary was everything I hoped it would be. We were given a small device which was basically our tour guide throughout the place. All the stories, and the history about the place somewhat made me wish I was a dreaded criminal in those days just so that I could live in Alcatraz with the worst of them. We were even locked in a cell for 30 seconds, the same cell where miscreants where locked up for a month or so. This cell had absolutely no sunlight. There were 6 of us in there and we could not see the person standing right next to us. The story goes that inmates locked up in that cell would throw a button on the floor and try to find it which would keep them occupied for the whole day. The next stop was the aquarium. I love wildlife, and love fish, and so this was another great experience for me. We were standing on a conveyer belt with sharks swimming over us. After grabbing a quick bite, we took a trolley ride of the entire city. Some of the sites left me speechless. The whole day turned out to be great in the end. The next 2 days we went to Hollywood where we stayed with another friend. We got an opportunity to visit Universal Studios. The tour of the studio was again fabulous. The special effects on the tour itself make you realize what these people go through to make movies. Can you imagine your tour trolley on a bridge, and suddenly the bridge starts shaking violently and King Kong emerges from one side? Or that you are in your trolley on the sets of a subway system and suddenly a helicopter crashes through and there is water everywhere? No wonder Bollywood is nowhere near Hollywood.

After a nice trip, we returned back to Boston. In the 5 months I was in the US, I had learned some pretty interesting facts about this country. I may have touched on these topics a bit earlier but I would like to elaborate here. One of the things I found fascinating and completely advantageous was that being of colored skin I could use the race card for pretty much everything. Now, I apologize to my brown/black friends for not keeping this a secret any more, but honestly Americans are so afraid of being called racist or anything even remotely close to that. If a girl in a club refuses a drink from me, all I have to say is, "Is it because I am brown?" And the girl will not only take that drink, but she will also dance with you just to prove that she is not racist. Reading this, a lot of my brown brothers might try to emulate me. My advice to you; don't. To pull these things of you need a certain swagger about you, and swagger is the last thing us Indians are born with. I am not saying I have it either. It is just that I happen to have a lot of practice. Please don't embarrass yourself. Other thing I really love about America is how they call the NBA, NFL and MLB winners the World Champions. For these teams to be World Champions, shouldn't there be teams from all over the world competing? But then again, there are teams from Canada in all those leagues and many Americans themselves will agree that the continental USA and Canada are pretty much the world for most of the country. Even shows like America's Got Talent proclaims the million-dollar prize for the winner to be the biggest in the world. Maybe monetarily it might be the biggest, but otherwise how can you call it the biggest prize in the world? Can the UN come in on this somehow? When I was in India, I used to think the advertisements on TV were so bad. Then I was introduced to the land of ads here in the US. I have new-found respect for ads in India now. You might find 1 in a 100 ads in the US that might actually make sense. Most of the ads are for medicines, and are quite funny. You see, in the US, you are supposed to mention the side effects of medicine in the ad itself which is great because even the doctors in India don't tell you about the side effects of medicines there. But on the downside, some of the side effects are crazier than the initial sickness itself. For example, this particular medicine for asthma which acts instantly, and is great is reducing you asthma attacks. However, side effects maybe include nausea, cold, stiffness, or HEART ATTACK. People suffering from depression have medicines which help reduce their depression*, however, side effects may include drowsiness, headaches, or feelings of SUICIDE. You know what? Thanks but I think I will stick to asthma and depression.

Spring 2007 brought another new experience for me; my first graduate *desi* party. I was invited by a friend whom I knew from my National College days, and he asked me to get Shilpa and my roommate Divya along too. As I entered, I saw that everyone was sitting in a circle, with around 4-5 girls here and there. The host was nice enough to take me around the circle

*Recently, German goalkeeper Robert Enke killed himself after a long battle with depression. RIP.

and introduce me to everyone there. Divya, Shilpa, and I decided to find a corner for ourselves and sip on our drinks. After a while, once everyone had enough drinks in them to lose all inhibitions, the music became loud and the crazy dancing started. And by crazy I mean crazy. Americans think 'screwing the light bulb' is the only move to all Hindi songs. They should really come to a *desi* party to see how insane and ridiculous some steps can be. Of course, I didn't join because to begin with the only form of dancing I know is grinding which I was sure Shilpa did not want to do there, and secondly at that point I also thought I was too cool for that crowd; an opinion I am glad has changed over time. Disturbingly, over my 3 years here in the US, I have realized that every *desi* party has the same pattern. Start off by sitting in a circle, drink like you want to die of alcohol poisoning, and then dance till you drop.

The new semester also had Rehan visit us in Boston. He was in Chicago working at that time, and I had not seen him for over 2 years now. I was really excited to see him. Also, I was excited to hear about his girlfriend, Soniya, whom he had started dating when they were together at the University of Southern California. Rehan was to stay at Megha's, and so Shilpa and I decided to stay at Megha's too for the weekend that he was here. It was great catching up with one of my closest friends, and also drinking like crazy with him which I had not done in ages. Also, I heard all the stories about Soniya who was an undergraduate student at USC, and how they started dating. Rehan even asked me to add her on Facebook, and MSN messenger as she wanted to talk to me too considering she had heard a lot about me. After Rehan left, I added Soniya and soon we started talking regularly on messenger. She was a great girl, with a great sense of humor, and I was really happy for Rehan.

Unfortunately, all this while, my relationship with Shilpa was really deteriorating. I could not put my finger on what was going wrong but I knew something was wrong. It was not only that I was getting some cold vibes from her, but I also did not have the strong feelings I once had for this girl. I just thought that the whole moving in together thing was affecting us a bit, and that it would get better with time. I was also a little jealous of the fact that she spent a lot of time with Crassy in the lab. I was not jealous of the guy as such, I mean come on he was nothing compared to me. But the fact that he was getting to spend more time with Shilpa than me was really pissing me off. One day, I was doing a double shift at my new job at the computer lab, and asked Shilpa to meet me for lunch in between the shifts so that I could at least spend 15 minutes of the day with her before we both hit the sack at night, all tired. To my disbelief, she ditched me and went for lunch with Crassy. What was I to take from this? I was really angry and this time I let her know how I felt. And her reply was, "I am so happy to see you angry. That makes me feel special." What the hell was wrong with this woman? I was insanely mad, and she tells me that my anger was making her feel special? Are all you women like this?

After that first major fight, we somehow managed to settle things down a bit. However, things were still not fine. It had reached a point where we weren't even indulging in physical activities. You know the relationship is not working when you are not having sex for long periods of time, especially when you are living together. One day Crassy had a party at his place, as he was moving to NY to work for a big financial company. Though I did not want to go, I went with Shilpa anyway and also thought that it was probably the last time that I would have to deal with this guy. After a few drinks, everyone started taking pictures but something happened and Shilpa started crying. I asked her what it was, and she told me that she was crying because Crassy didn't consider her a good friend or something. I knew this was getting ridiculous. It was high time I dumped this woman, a woman who had never given me any respect in our relationship, and move on. But all you guys know me by now. Not only don't I have any self-respect, I also don't have the balls to breakup with someone. So I chose to ignore that situation and said goodbye to Crassy for good. However, within a couple of weeks after Crassy left, Shilpa started insisting that she wanted to go to NY to visit Namrata and also meet Crassy. Usually she drags me along, however, this time she wasn't insistent on that either. She even suggested that she might stay over at Crassy's place one night. Just for the record, this girl was my girlfriend at that time, and Crassy had a girlfriend too who was in India and was planning to come to Boston the following year for her MBA. I told Shilpa that there was no way I was going to let her stay at a guy's house, especially a guy whom I had such of a problem with. Don't get me wrong, this guy was a good friend but I knew Shilpa had some feelings for him and I didn't want something to go down; or up in his pants. Despite of me telling her not to go, Shilpa left that weekend to NY. I even picked up the phone a couple of times to end things, but I just couldn't do it. The first night, she stayed over with Namrata. However, the next night both of them went over to Crassy's house to stay. The next day I got a long email from Shilpa, basically saying that things were over between us. This girl had just ended a one and a half year relationship over email. And I thought I was a coward.

Anecdote : Necrophiliac

I don't want to give you the wrong impression here, and let me clarify that I have no fantasies about having sex with cadavers. However, once I did do it with something that you might be able to classify as a corpse. Back in India, Shilpa's parents had gone out of town and we had a few friends over at her place. All of us got drunk, and Shilpa was completely hammered. She dragged me into her room and did some "fun activities". I soon started hearing this new sound, a sound she was making and had never made before. I was kind of happy that I was maybe pleasing her in a new way and that she was really happy. Though that bubble was soon burst as I realized that she was sleeping, and the sound was her snoring. Not knowing what to do, I stopped. But as soon as I did, she woke up and asked me, "Why are you stopping? Keep going!" Of course as soon as I resumed, she was back in deep slumber. But this time I decided to keep at it and finish up before going to a nice peaceful night of sleep.

Hoes before bros : Part I

Getting dumped over email is the most ridiculous thing ever, and I had just been dumped like that. I was sitting in the computer lab when I checked my email, fully expecting an email from Shilpa ending things. Shilpa had not called me that entire day from New York, and in the evening she called asking me if I had checked my email. When I said no, she asked me to check it and then call her so we could talk. I did not have to be a rocket scientist to figure out what was going to be in the email she had sent. So when I actually opened that email, and read through it, I did not react much to it. I walked out of the lab as calmly as possible, and went to the student cafeteria to grab something to eat. I decided to call Shilpa then. As soon as I heard her voice, something went wrong and I just could not hold it in anymore. I burst out in tears, begging her to give me another chance. There are two things completely wrong with this picture. First and foremost, I did not even want to be in this relationship and yet I was crying. I think more than anything it was my ego being hurt by this girl dumping me; a girl I wanted to end things with. Second of all, crying in front of the girl who just ended your relationship is the worst thing you can ever do. It just confirms the girl's decision of ending it because you are proving to be such a loser. Word of advice to all my men out there: When dumped, always act like you don't care. Your woman will run back to you because they are messed up creatures who will not feel good about the breakup until they have really hurt you.

Unfortunately for me, I was forgetting my own rule and crying out rivers in a public place. She showed no remorse and told me that she would be staying with Crassy for a few more days because she did not want to see me right now. At that point, it hit me like a freight train; she had dumped me for another guy. After she hung up, I called Mona, a mutual friend of ours to the cafeteria and started crying to her. Mona comforted me and told me that it will all be ok, and that Shilpa was just a bit confused and that she just needs to clear her head up. After a couple of days, I saw Shilpa online. I asked her why she was not coming home and if something had happened between her and Crassy. She kept denying it at first and then admitted that they had made out one night after she broke up with me. I should have expected something like this from a girl who jumped from relationship to relationship, but I did not expect this from a guy who was one of my good friends at Northeastern. In the email, Shilpa had told me that she did not see me having a future. Considering I had just completed one semester in my masters program, how was anyone to see what the future had to hold? Was she psychic that she knew I would be a failure? I later figured out that when women say "future", what they really mean is 'you are broke you asshole, and I need someone who can pamper me and take care of me'. And this is exactly what this girl meant too. I had not been able to pamper her as much as I could in India. And now there was this guy who was working at a big financial firm, with an apartment overlooking the New York skyline. And more importantly, as Shilpa told me later, a guy who did not give her attention which made her want him more. This was so brilliant. I actually hated this guy but I respected him because he used the oldest trick in the book and made it work to perfection. Basically, Shilpa had a choice between me, a guy who gave her anything she wished for if it was in my financial capability, and this other guy who had all the money a girl could need but did not give her any attention whatsoever. It was never a competition! But even after realizing all this, my ego still didn't accept the fact that this girl had just ended it with me. I had to do anything to get her back.

After a week, Shilpa finally came back to Boston. I was in the angry phase then, and completely ignored her the first few days. Also, I was in the getting drunk every night and smoking regularly phase. A lot of guys do this, especially Indian guys. I firmly believe this is inspired by the Bollywood movie Devdas, where the hero loses the love of his life and starts drinking till he dies. Though it might sound extremely romantic, the bottom-line is that the guy was a loser who drank himself to death, with an emphasis on death. And again, you are just helping the girl justify her decision of dumping your sorry ass. But who am I to judge Devdas when I was doing the same thing? It had been 4 days since Shilpa had got back from New York, and we still hadn't spoken a single word. We were still in the same apartment, but at nights I would sleep over at Pramod's house. One day, however, I was sitting on my desktop and Shilpa on the bed in our room, when she told me that we needed to talk. I did not know what to say but all this pent up anger came out again in the form of tears. I think I cried more tears during this whole period than the annual rainfall the Amazon rainforest gets annually.

I really wanted to tell her how I should have expected it from someone like her, but I ended up saying how nice she was and how she deserved to be with someone better. The following days were filled torturous with me trying to be friends with her, and doing everything possible for her to make her come back to me, and her trying to spend more time with Crassy. Speaking of Crassy, one fine day, just a few days after all this shit had gone down, Shilpa handed me her phone and told me Crassy wanted to talk to me. I reluctantly took the phone and asked him what he wanted. He said that he did not expect things to happen the way things did but he wanted us to still be friends and me to come over to his place with Shilpa who was to visit him that weekend. What a douche! Did he really expect me to be friends with him, especially after he had kissed Shilpa just a day after we had broken up? Yeah, he had made the first move. He had kissed her when they were sitting together. And now he wanted to be friends? I used up all the abuses I had in my vocabulary in that particular conversation. And while I kept saying things to the effect of your momma is so fat, she had to be baptized at sea-world, he kept asking me to be civil. Did this guy really expect me to be civil after what he had done? Also, he brought up examples of what he would have done right in certain situation with Shilpa that I did not handle correctly. For example, there was this one time when Namrata was visiting us from New York and Shilpa, Namrata, Crassy, a friend Varun, and I decided to go to a club. We got a cab and I got in the front. There were four people in the back, and Shilpa decided to sit on Varun's lap. The next day, Shilpa told Crassy and me that she felt like Varun was running his hands on her thighs and feeling her thighs up but she wasn't sure about it. Crassy pointed out during our conversation after the breakup that he would have confronted Varun if he was

Shilpa's boyfriend. What do you tell a fool who doesn't realize that the fault was not in Varun's hands, which Shilpa was not even sure about, but the fact that Shilpa decided to sit on Varun's lap when her childhood friend was sitting right next to Varun. What exactly did she expect sitting on a drunken guy's lap? And there is no way I was going to question a good friend over something my promiscuous girlfriend was not even sure about. I hung up on Crassy instead of telling him why I did not react how he would have just because he was trying to act macho in front of his new-found love, and just walked away from Shilpa too. I wish I had just shut her out from my life, but I just couldn't let go that easily.

All this drama was really close to Tarang, the Indian festival at Northeastern University. Shilpa was to perform on stage with a few other girls and so I was to go for this event too. Keeping up with the tradition of pre-gaming before any event, I went over to Pramod's place and we had a few rounds of Jack Daniels. Then we headed to Tarang. It was to be held in a ballroom. At this point, I would really like to share some interesting things about this fantastic event. You know for a fact that the students who come in early to get seats up ahead to get a good view are usually new students who have never been to Tarang before. The older, experienced students always come in early to grab seats at the back. Why you ask? Well Tarang is the only event on the planet where people come in early to grab seats at the back because the food is served at the back. Who doesn't love free food but we Indians love it a bit too much. So much so that the amount of food each student takes in their plate is just unfathomable. It really looks like a bunch of underprivileged kids from Somalia just got off the flight to the US and found out that there was free food being served at Northeastern. As soon as the presenter for the night announces that food is now being served, the line formed is almost instantaneous, and it extends to well outside the ballroom. I am pretty confident that some of them even starve themselves for a few days before coming for this event. The show of course has the same stuff they had back in India, comprising of a million dances, couple of singers, a fashion show, and a standup comedian. Dances are good, but do you really want to show off so many of them? I mean Americans anyway think we are a bunch of lunatics who break out into a song and dance at every opportunity, and by performing so many dances we are just adding fuel to that fire.

Some singers are good, but some should just stick to singing when they are taking a dump or when taking a shower. The fashion shows in India were bad enough as I have described earlier, but here they take it to the next level of intolerable. The good part about these so-called fashion shows back in India were that though they had lame choreography and clothes owned by the "models" themselves, these models were at least good looking, or relatively good looking. At Northeastern, everyone is given an opportunity to participate. So men and women who would never be taken a second glance at take this God given chance to showcase themselves. I usually wanted to rip my eyes out after watching those. And finally the standup comedian is just never funny. My first year at Tarang, the guy doing standup came up with this joke: When I go home, I yell to my roommates, "Honey, I'm home!" That was it. That was the joke. When he said it, I think everyone was waiting for him to say the punch line and all he did was looked up at the crowd and started laughing at his own joke, proud that he had come up with that brilliant joke himself. Ever since Russell Peters became famous, I think every Indian sees a Russell in them. What is more irritating than a bad standup comedian are a couple of presenters trying to crack jokes in between two shows. I understand the main purpose of these presenters are to act as fillers between two dances or two shows as such, but please don't make that period even more painful by talking. I would rather have a mime crack jokes than you people trying to entertain me.

Coming back to Tarang in 2007, Pramod and I entered to a full ballroom. The show started and soon the crowd began to go wild over all dances, and the entire crowd somehow knew how to whistle which is of course the best form of encouragement. After a couple of dances, the presenter announced that the food was now being served. No sooner had I heard that, the line had already formed and all the food was gone too. In the end, I had to go through the plates of people I barely knew to eat something. And everyone whose plate I raided had a meal fitting for a king in that little plate. Shilpa's dance was up next and it was a one-minute thing which they had practiced for 2 months. As soon as her dance was over, we left and headed home. It was the last day at that house for Shilpa as she was moving out. The next day, I helped her pack all her stuff, and by afternoon we were about to start moving stuff when suddenly Shilpa starts crying and says, "This is not how we had planned things. This is not how things were supposed to happen." YOU THINK? If only you did not have to sleep around so much, we would still be together. Of course, all these were statements made in my head. But then I did something that I thought I could never do; something just brilliant. I pretended to start crying. Yeah, I faked crying! I know it is despicable but hey this chic was sleeping around with my friend within a day of us breaking up so she was obviously the epitome of despicable. Seeing me cry made her feel really bad, and she told me that we should definitely stay in touch and be friends in spite of Crassy ordering her not to even talk to me ever. She even told me that she would miss me. This was the perfect opportunity for me to use the oh-so-famous line from Gone With The Wind: "Frankly my dear, I don't give a damn." But I think it is well established by now that God played a cruel joke on me and forgot to give me a set of balls. So I hugged her and said goodbye.

Goodbye for the day that is. Shilpa was now living about 10 minutes from my place so we still met up every day. As a matter of fact, she would even sleep over sometimes when my new roommate, a guy from Kerala here on a work project, was away. This girl was completely using me to feel less guilty about dumping me for my friend. She would even call me late in the night to tell me she was cold or she was hungry, and I would run over with a blanket or food. This went on for a month, and in a couple of week's time it was her birthday. In the past, I had wooed her with thoughtful gifts on her birthday. So I thought that this year I had to outdo myself, and that might just tip the scales in my favor somehow. I came up with making a video for Shilpa with all her friends all over the US and back home, her parents, the SNFT clan, some of my friends and my mom. Pretty soon all the participants started sending in their videos. Some friends just wished her a very happy birthday, while some wished her more creatively.

Her mom had a video where she was talking about how Shilpa was as a child, and in the process starts crying. Shilpa's sister even sent in a video of her dog Duster. The SNFT clan did one of the best videos in preparing this hilarious skit. I had to come up with something good. I thought of singing Don McLean's American Pie because she always made me sing it. It is not that I am a good singer; I never was and never will be. It was just that, during that Lonavala trip with the SNFT clan, we were singing this song together and it had since become our song. Also, I decided to do a little dance on the song *Say Na Say Na* from the Bollywood movie Bluffmaster, a remake of the Hollywood movie Matchstick Men.

I compiled the video and showed it to her on her birthday. It brought tears to her eyes. You know you did well when the girl is crying, in a non-sadistic way of course. Shilpa soon left for India to visit her family. By this time, I had a new roommate. And as my luck would have it, a guy from Delhi. I was nice enough to show him around the neighborhood a bit, but he mistook this for us being friends. Every day, he would come home and ask me how my day was. It was like we were married, and had to tell each other everything that happened. I would usually say nothing much and get back to whatever I was doing, but this guy would tell me each and every detail of his day. I really think he wanted me to put it up his ass. I started calling Shilpa everyday to bitch about the new Delhiite in my life. One thing women love is a bitching partner. One day she told me that she was going to hang out with the SNFT people that night. The very next day, I got a call from my friend Hasnain in that group, telling me that she was a bit unhappy in her relationship with Crassy and that I should keep trying. Apparently, though Crassy was a successful man, he also had this amazing quality of abuse. He had slapped Shilpa because of her past relationships. Thinking that any self-respecting girl wouldn't take that shit, I started calling Shilpa more often. But one day she told me not to call again as Crassy didn't want her talking to me, and that she really wanted to make things work with him. She wanted to make it work with a guy who had slapped her. And I thought I was the one with self-respect issues. More than anything, I think this girl was afraid of being alone. I lost all respect I had for that woman and completely blocked her from my life.

After the breakup, the most sensible thing for anyone to do is obviously to find a rebound, and to find it fast. There are two things to be done after a breakup. First, have a one-night stand to get your ex-partner out of your system. Second, have a rebound relationship so that you can at least fake feelings for someone else for a while and not think about your ex. To achieve these things, I started flirting with a lot of women I knew, women who found me attractive. One of those women was Allie, the girl who had accused me of hitting on her back in India. Allie was in school at USC, and was dating a guy. However, she definitely responded to my flirting and used to flirt back as well. As a matter of fact, we were really hitting it off. She was soon to come to Boston for a job interview, and I was really hoping this visit would get the one-night stand I needed out of the way. We made plans to meet up at the hotel she was staying at the night before her interview. I always believe that interviewees and students who have exams coming up should be provided with condoms just like athletes in the Olympics or any other meet. Not only will students look forward to exam time, they will actually be relaxed for it. Unfortunately, no one was there to provide me with free condoms, and I did not trust the ones you got for free in the health centre or the ones in vending machines. So I went to get a box from the nearest CVS Pharmacy. Rehan had told me that usually they are kept behind the checkout counter and so I went up to the lady and asked for condoms. She told me that they were in the aisle that said "Family Planning", which made sense of course, but would be glad to help me out. To help me, she switched on the public announcement system and said, "Condoms to counter 2 please. Condoms to counter 2." I really wish the person who got me the packet would have got me a knife instead so I could have stabbed myself to death at that moment. And for all the embarrassment, I ended up paying $15. I could get the same packet for Rs.100 in India. Too bad for me that my dad was to pack my suitcases when I was to fly to the US, or else I would have made sure I brought a lifetime supply of condoms; meaning two packets.

Off I went to Framingham, Massachusetts to satiate my thirst for a one-night stand. I arrived at Framingham and in no time was at the hotel. I hadn't seen this girl in a while but I was definitely excited, for obvious reasons. I went up to her room, knocked and waited for her to open. She opened and I was glad I had come. Again, she was not the best looking girl but looking at her body standing outside the door to her room was enough to confirm that I had made the correct decision in coming to the hotel. She was short but had a ratio that any woman would be proud of, and I was proud of it too. We hugged and I was invited in. The next few moments were spent in making small talk, extremely awkward small talk if I may add. If my memory serves me right, we even spoke about issues in the Middle East. Then she called for a burger and some fries that we could share as both of us were hungry. There was a reason why I was hungry. I usually don't like to have a full stomach before any physical activity. You don't want your stomach to be popping out. On an empty stomach, I can at least boast about having a couple of abdominal muscles. However, I guess she did not care about any of this. While we were consuming the delicious burger, she started talking about how she met her boyfriend.

Why in the world would any girl who is just about to cheat on her boyfriend talk about him? Something really caught my attention in her story though. Apparently, the first time her boyfriend had seen Allie, he thought she was the hottest woman he had seen. Either this guy needed some glasses, or had some low standards when it came to hot women, or maybe his definition of hot was just different. Anyway, I chuckled in my head and just let that slide by. After we were done, we slipped in under the blankets and I tried to kiss her. I say tried because she rejected me! SHE rejected ME. She said she couldn't cheat on her boyfriend! I had been talking to this woman for a long time now, travelled for an hour, listened to her stories, and all this so I could just lie down next to her and sleep? I wanted to tell her that a majority of boyfriends would consider it cheating if their girlfriends just slept with another guy in the same bed. However, I was too annoyed to say anything and just decided to sleep.

After maybe an hour of falling asleep cuddling up with Allie, I felt her leg rubbing against my manhood. She was awake and was just rubbing her leg against me. I took this opportunity to kiss her but again she turned away. This time, however, I decided to go ahead with other things even though she was not kissing me, and she readily obliged. But throughout the whole time, she didn't kiss me even once. Maybe she believed that by kissing me she would actually be cheating on her boyfriend. Well here is a newsflash for you Allie; having some guy over for the night in your hotel room is classified as cheating. Also, I love satisfying my woman in bed. I always make sure her needs are taken care of, and that she gets the feeling of being on top of the world at least once, if not more, and I did the same thing that night too. Just when I was close to me being the king of the world, Allie begs for me to stop because she had gotten an orgasm again and she could not take it anymore. I do all this work and I don't even get any satisfaction? So it was back to cuddling up and sleeping again. The next morning, her boyfriend woke her up for her interview, while I was next to her in bed. After an hour we both left the hotel, her to go to the interview, and me to go unsatisfied back to my place. The guy sitting at the counter at the bus station at Framingham was the same Indian guy from the previous night. He looks at me and says, "That was a short visit." I smiled and got on bus.

Now that I had my one-night stand out of the way, almost, I could focus on other things. I had no friends at Northeastern. The only friends I had, and I really hung out with were Shilpa, Crassy and Pramod. The former two were now in "love", while the latter had moved far away from school leaving me a loner. As a result, I decided to mingle more with my peeps, the Indians. I met some great friends in this process. Vishwesh Patil, Nikhil Bhatia, Vishwas Pathak were some of the guys whom I used to find uncouth at one point but now was having a blast with. And they were guys whom I knew would always be there for me, and would not screw my girlfriend ever. But in the process of making new friends, I also came across some very interesting characters. There was a guy who said "Come on" to everything. Dude you want to go for a movie? Come on! Hey you want to grab a beer? Come on! Dude wait for me, I need to take a dump. Come on! Though I do think that was a great way to end an argument. You guys agree with me don't you? Come on! Come on! Come on! Then there was a girl who hugged her way through life. She was busty and I know you can get a lot of things from guys if you have big honkers and keep hugging every other guy but shouldn't there be some sort of a filter as to whom you hug? No matter who the guy was, or what he looked like, if this girl had some work with him, the guy would surely get something against his chest. But it did help her in a way. She made it to the supervisor position at the computer lab in no time. If only I had a nice rack *sigh*.

But my favorite person was a guy called Ass. Physically, Ass was almost as tall as me but was overweight. Now that guy had a nice rack. But this weight issue never dimmed his enthusiasm. He was always at the forefront of events, dancing his ass off. He was an extremely positive person, who would have been an inspiration for many, if only he could stop lying.

This guy was the biggest liar the planet had ever seen. When all of us were struggling about for an internship, this guy tells everyone that he rejected an offer for an internship with State Street because he thought the company was not big enough for him. Also, after graduation, we were led to believe that an extraordinary GMAT score had secured him an admit from Kellog's Business School which was the reason why he had given up a full time job offer at Google. I would readily have a threesome with Sergey Brin and Lawrence Page to get a job at Google and this guy had rejected an offer there. Of course he had not got any MBA admission either. Maybe he was just being sarcastic about his situation and all of us misunderstood him. If that is the case, we need to take some lessons in sarcasm from this man.

As a member of the Indian community, I was also forced to play the summer cricket tournament held by Sanskriti. I am a good sportsman, but cricket would be the last sport I would want to play. Watching me play cricket would be like watching a dyslexic child at a spelling bee; just painful. I was ridiculed a lot during the course of the tournament by people I would look down upon. That is when I realized that no matter how cool I thought I was, everyone would be better than me in one way or the other, in something or the other, and I had to accept that and try to lower the ego I had. Screw that, I was still cooler than them. Also, I started attending more *desi* parties. And for some reason, as I was single now, guys had a problem with me talking to their girlfriends. After having a few drinks, I like to chat with the opposite sex and I really get into it. If I want to talk to a guy, why the hell would

I want to drink before that? Unfortunately, people around me think I am hitting on the person I am talking to. Just because I am having an interesting conversation with a woman does not mean I am hitting on them. Especially if that woman is related to anyone I know, or if she is dating someone I know. Nikhil once explained to me that the guys were intimidated by me because they believed I looked better than them and could carry myself much better. Basically I was to sit in a corner at parties, talk to guys, and not have fun because they are really insecure. Now I hated Shilpa and Crassy more for making me go through this.

Also, one thing that Indian graduate students love doing is gossiping. Considering that most of the students just take 2 classes each semester, which means only a couple of 3-hour lectures in a week. So leaving aside the 20 hours you worked on campus in a week, you had a lot of free time. Free time = bitching. I even heard that people talked about my breakup and that I deserved it because I used to torment Shilpa when I was drunk; physically and mentally. If anything, I was the one abused in that relationship. This one guy Sagar D., who was a bigger bitch than my brother's younger dog Iris, even told people that he once saw Shilpa stripping for me. Though I wish that were true, it was far from reality. If only I had a good friend to talk to through my breakup. To really let someone know how I felt. Rehan was always there for me and so was his girlfriend Soniya. But guys don't really pour their hearts out to guys, and Soniya was close but not close enough for me to tell her exactly how I was feeling. That was where Neha Mishra came into the picture.

Neha had come in to Northeastern a semester after I had, and was dating a friend of mine. We started working together at the computer lab and soon became really good friends. I would actually look forward to working because of her. She was definitely cute and I did have a small crush on her but there was no way I would have done anything considering she was dating a friend. There are some things you just don't do. I definitely did not want to be a Crassy in someone else's life and be the cause of the end of their relationship. It was great to have such good friend around especially in those tumultuous times, when my life was a complete mess. One day while we were working together, Neha called me over to the computer she was sitting at and asked me to take a look at the screen. On the screen, I saw me, Anish Sadanandan, chatting to her on Gtalk, telling her how much I loved her.

It was insane. Only Rehan knew I kind of had a crush on this girl but there was no way anyone else would know. Suddenly I realized what was happening. I used to leave my Gmail logged in on my desktop in my room, and someone was using it. Not only that, if they had been using it, they had been using it since quite some time because they had read my chats. I made a stupid mistake of typing in that chat window, "This is Anish. Who the hell is this?" As soon as I said that, the person went offline. I ran home, and found that Doggy was the only one home. I questioned her regarding this and she told me that her roommate's boyfriend was home and that he was using my computer. Sadly for Doggy, I knew the guy she was talking about and he was working at the library at that time. What kind of a person does something like that? You have to be totally jobless and have no life to go through someone's chats, and then try to talk to a girl I would never ever think of going out with and convince her that I was in love with her.

I gave Doggy an earful, including a lot of obscenities. She actually threatened me that if I were to curse again, she would call the cops and tell them I was physically abusing her and that they would believe me because she was a woman. This girl had been watching too many Hindi movies in her life, or maybe police in Delhi just took the woman's side. Doggy even once tried to convince a cab driver that she was a weak woman and that he should help her carry her luggage up to our apartment. The cab driver got pissed off at her and told her he wasn't her servant and drove away. This girl was even in chanting 3 times a day and I had no clue what kind of voodoo she was into and I did not want to be a victim of some spells. I just let it go and did not ever talk to that witch again. For some reason, my friendship with Neha deteriorated. It had nothing to do with this incident but over time it just faded and at this point we don't even talk. Neha, if you are reading this, I have no idea what I did to offend you but whatever I did I am really sorry about it and wish you could forgive me for it. It sucks to not have you as a friend in my life.

Now that I had my mingling with my community out of the way as well, it was time for me to look for a rebound relationship. After the breakup, I had started flirting with a lot of women back in India. I know it did not make sense but some of them were planning to come to the US for their higher studies. One was Roma, one was a girl I was dating when I was younger, but the girl that was really responding to my advances was The Twin.

Anecdote : Doggy style

Dogs are a man's best friends. God was not exactly kind to dogs considering they are colorblind, have a lifespan of around 12-15 years max, have no sweat glands, and can smell food in their own poop. However, God did give them something that would make them forget about all the other shortcomings, and that was doggy style position. It is one of the best sexual positions and dogs should be proud that there is a position named after them. But we humans have stolen it from our canine friends and we use it to the fullest. Can you imagine how disappointed your dog must feel? They had one thing that they could boast about and now we humans do it too. To add to that, some of the dogs actually have to watch their masters do it in their position. How annoying must that be for them? Can you imagine walking in on your dog and seeing him hump in missionary position? How disturbing will it be for you? So next time you think of going doggy, think of your doggy.

Doing Mary

I call this girl The Twin because that is what she was known as in and around D. J. Sanghvi College of Engineering. The Twin was a year junior to Shilpa, making her two years my junior, and looked remarkably similar to Shilpa. And to add to rumors that they were actually related, both of them were in the fashion show together as well. I remember the first time I saw The Twin in the fashion show. She was in black and looked absolutely stunning. So stunning that I actually took her mental picture, to use later that night. As a matter of fact, I used to find The Twin hotter than Shilpa, but of course I never admitted to that. Shilpa had once introduced me to her Siamese twin after a function in college, telling the doppelganger that I found her extremely attractive. So in the end, Shilpa had laid the foundation for me to flirt with this girl. So I suppose she wasn't that bad for me after all.

After my breakup, as I mentioned before, I flirted with every girl I even remotely knew and to my relief The Twin was more than responding. I even told her the details about how Shilpa had dumped me so that I could get sympathy points. We started talking on the phone everyday though we were in different countries, which did cost me a lot of money on calling cards if I may add. She was dating this guy who most of us thought was gay because he looked exactly like his sister*, but had now ended things with him. I had an opening alright, and I utilized it to the fullest. The Twin told me how she had

---

*They would have been perfect for the roles of Viola and Sebastian Hastings in the movie She's The Man.

never owned a Barbie doll, and so guess what my gift was for her birthday a month after we started talking so much? She absolutely loved the doll and my points just kept on rising. One day, I went to another one of the "awesome" *desi* parties, and after having a lot of alcohol, called India and asked The Twin out. Why would a girl ever say yes to a guy who asks her out after getting shit drunk? It is like a guy agreeing to impregnate a woman who says she wants a baby after she is drunk. Anyway, I was in a relationship, again. I met my brother on Gtalk the next day and told him to tell me that I was stupid. Without any questions asked, he said, "You are stupid."

Now that I was in a "relationship", I could focus on some extracurricular activities as well. I was always a football player and so I decided to start playing some pickup game of futsal or football, whichever was going on the day I would be free. As soon as I started playing with these African, Spanish, French, Turkish, American, and kids from many other nationalities, I realized why India was ranked so low in the FIFA football rankings. I had honestly come to the US with the hopes of getting a football scholarship, but man did I get a rude awakening. These kids were so good, and they were not even making to the club team. The main college team is the varsity team, and then the next level is the club team. I tried out for the club team the first year and soon realized that I should just give up football. Everyone was just running and dribbling past me as if I did not exist. It was more painful than watching Kanye West getting up on stage drunk during the VMA awards ceremony. At first, no one would even pass the ball to me because I was Indian and no one had ever heard of an Indian football play. Biachung Bhutia, I am sorry but playing for Bury didn't really make you that famous. Slowly, I started learning that the game was way more physical than back home, and that I had to get more physical just to keep up with these guys. I started working out just for this and soon started shoving around the thin white kids to begin with. After a while, I got used to all their moves and even started pulling off some of my own. Some of the guys were shocked when I told them that I had just been in the US for a few months because they were amazed a guy from India could actually play good football.

Football kept me busy, and so did the long distance relationship with The Twin. For those who think I am a moron for getting into a long distance, well this girl was to come to Carnegie Mellon for her masters in a few months and so we would be in the same country, on the same coast, though different states and so long distance. Hence proved that I am, in fact, a moron. Rehan had, in the meanwhile, moved to New Jersey to join one of the Indian consulting firms. This is a last ditch resort taken by many PIGS to stay in the US, if they don't find a job after graduation. What these consulting companies do is that they train you on some software, or in some programming language, make a fake resume for you which would have at least 5 years worth experience in the particular industry they are going to train you in, and then finally market you to American firms that have no clue what in the world is happening. But Rehan living in New Jersey meant that I could meet Mary Jane for my birthday and strike off the final never-to-do thing from my list. Rehan met MJ almost every day and he would tell me how amazing she was. So I decided to give it a shot for my birthday. He came over to Boston just on the fateful day my mother had given birth to me 24 years earlier* with Mary. At the Penn State train station in New York, he was "randomly" selected for a search. He had hid Mary in his football shoe and so somehow managed to make it through the search without getting caught.

Once he reached Boston, we sat down at my place, and then he introduced me to MJ. At first I could not feel her, but after some time I realized how amazing a person she actually was. We hit a club after that, and that too a club with house music and insane lights. That is when MJ really showed her true colors. Her absurd grip on me made sure that no matter how much I drank that night, I would be happy high.

After meeting MJ, I wanted to meet her regularly. Let me assure you it was no addiction in any sort of way. Meeting MJ with Rehan was the most enjoyable thing I had done in my life. We would talk absolute crap after the rendezvous, with topics ranging from how we could be awesome basketball players, to how Sylar was the most powerful man on the planet, to bitching about women which of course was always fun even if you are not high. After all the bullshit, Edison, New Jersey offered a variety of amazing Indian food for the insane food craving you get after romancing Mary. Edison is a very Indian neighborhood. As a matter of fact, I would say it is more Indian than India itself. There are sari stores, Mahatma Gandhi malls, *paan* shops, and a great deal of Indian and Pakistani

*When I was born, my mother cried for almost an hour or so because (A) I was not a girl as she wanted and (B) I was a very ugly kid.

food places. There are even those old ladies who stare you down if you are smoking in public. We went to this Indian restaurant once to pick up some food, and as I started paying for it by card, one guy behind the counter starts telling the other guy with him how paying by cards should not be allowed because customers never leave tips. It was the lamest trick in the book to get some tip, but I was way too high to make fun of him and ended up giving him a really generous tip. Poor guy must still be using that line thinking it was successful with me. All in all, we were having a blast in New Jersey. One day, after getting high, Rehan announced that he wanted to speak to The Twin. I called her and gave the phone to Rehan. After talking to her for 5 minutes, Rehan handed me back the phone saying that he could not talk to the girl anymore because she was really dumb, and that he could not relate to her; all this while she was still on the phone. Luckily, she didn't hear a word of his comments, and I quickly hung up to ponder over what Rehan had said. This girl was dumb alright. Academically, she was doing great, but that is not really the kind of smartness you are looking for in a relationship. Usually, you are looking for someone who is smart enough to have great conversations with, someone who is street smart, and this girl was far from it. What had I gotten myself into?

By summer of 2007, I was really beginning to enjoy myself. My football playing prowess had gotten me an offer from a division II football team in the Massachusetts State Football League (MSSL) called BUA FC. BUA was founded by an Irish guy named McCormick and a couple of other

Americans. McCormick was a typical Irish guy; tall, strong, cursed the hell out of everyone and everything, played dirty, physical football, and could drink till all the alcohol in a bar was over. I made some great friends in that team and McCormick and Leon were a couple of them. Apart from matches, we even used to go out quite often to bars and have a few drinks. Once we went out with some of the guys from the team, along with our new goalkeeper Victor. Victor had a hot girlfriend, whose nude pictures were shown to us by him very proudly. But Victor was also a very promiscuous guy who believed he was in an open relationship. So while at this one bar that night, with his hot girlfriend, Vic slapped this black chic's butt really hard. We were sure the girl would turn around and slap him, but this girl just turned around and smiled. I guess being Argentinean kind of helped him. As he was busy with other girls that night, I was talking to his girlfriend the whole time and I was actually enjoying my conversation with her. She was a great girl, looked great, and to top it off was a football player! What more could you want in a girl? Unfortunately, I was seeing someone and she was seeing a guy I knew so it would have been inane to try flirting with her. After she left for home, all the guys headed to a club nearby, and as soon as we entered we realized it was lesbian night at the club. Though there were some really hot girls in there, the guys knew it was futile to try anything. However, as we stood outside smoking, a couple of our extremely drunk mates decided to break up a lesbian pairing and keep the pieces to themselves. One girl came up to us and asked us if she could borrow a smoke to which the guy said, "Forget the cigarette, want to look at my cigar?" The girl smiled and politely replied,

"Honey, if you are looking for pussy, you ain't gonna find any here."

That summer was also more exciting for me because The Twin was to come to Boston a month before her school started to spend some time with her brother who lived in Cambridge. This was my rebound relationship and I had to develop some fake emotions for this girl too so that I could get over Shilpa. Of course, when the rebound ends you just start thinking about your ex again but still it is suppose to help a bit, if not completely, in helping you get over someone. I was trying to make myself believe that I liked this girl but it was really hard after Rehan said she was dumb. Every time I tried to think positively, I would remember the face Rehan made when he told me about her intelligence. However, cometh the day she was supposed to come to Boston and I was excited. I had spoken to her sister-in-law and she told me that The Twin's brother and herself would pick me up from my place and go to the airport. Meeting the brother is always tricky business, and this time I was going to have to hold the fort on my won without any sort of support from the girl. On the drive to the airport, I tried my best to crack some jokes and make him laugh but I could barely get a chuckle out of him. I don't blame him. I was kind of nervous, and in that nervousness, my jokes seemed more like the ones attempted by the standup comedian at Tarang. I could kind of empathize with him now. Her sister-in-law was kind enough to laugh and not make me feel more awkward. We picked The Twin up from the airport, and she was genuinely surprised to see me there. While dropping me to my place, she got out and gave me a nice long hug. It was a good start to the "relationship".

The Twin's brother, Deshmukh, had asked me to come over for dinner the next day. I was happy he had but again it meant talking to him which made me a tad uncomfortable. I went over with a 6-pack of Heineken thinking that by the end of the 6-pack, both of us would be relaxed enough and we could have a nice conversation. I reach her place to find out that her brother doesn't drink. I nervously sipped on my beer while he asked me questions pertaining to my field of study, which if someone asks me even now I would not be able to explain as I myself am not sure about it. Dinner was a bit better as Deshmukh's wife was less of a grouch and she was more than happy to make the bulk of the conversation. As I was about to leave, The Twin offered to walk me down. This was the first time we were going to be alone together and I instantly forgot all the awkwardness I had just been through and put some lip balm on without anyone noticing. Many Indian guys think using chapsticks is pretty gay, but on the contrary my fellow brown brothers, it is good to use a chapstick. You don't want your lips to be dry while kissing a girl, do you? It would be like kissing someone's dry feet from those dry and cracked foot skin cream ads you see on TV all the time. How would you like that? I was ready with my moisturized lips while waiting for the elevator. No sooner had The Twin joined me, I had my hands around her waist, holding her from behind. We got into the elevator and as soon as the doors closed, I kissed her. It was a very intense kiss, and The Twin turned out to be a way better kisser than Shilpa. First kisses always make a very big impression, and The Twin's kiss had just made me forget Rehan's statement about her. It was absolutely amazing and I could not stop kissing her even when the elevator doors had opened. We walked outside and I leaned against a car. She leaned in to kiss me again. I guess I had made a good first impression too. We stood outside for around half-an-hour before we decided to split ways, not before making plans for a Hindi movie the next day. Some of my friends from Northeastern were supposed to go watch some stupid movie the next day. I was more than happy to invite The Twin along, especially after the incredible kiss. I was given a ride by my friend Mona and her fiancée, and we picked up The Twin from her home in Cambridge. After the brief introductions in the car, we were soon at it again in the backseat. I did feel a bit bad for Mona and her fiancée but then again I had to take care of my needs too. I would never want to make out with a girl in the presence on my *desi* peeps but Mona and her fiancée were cool like that. After the movie, we dropped the Twin home but now I needed to take this to the next level. I was getting too restless.

We did not meet the next day as it was a Sunday but did make plans to meet up at her brother's place on Monday. I knew I might not get to go all the way that soon but I would get to second base at least. I have to admit I enjoy foreplay a lot. Actually, I am really good at it so maybe that is the reason why I like it so much. I went over to Deshmukh's on Monday and she was there all-alone, looking fabulous in a brown top. While getting down to business, I kept thinking to myself about my theory on how the physical part in a relationship is so important, and this so-called relationship was completely proving that. This girl was great from the physical standpoint but there was no mental connection whatsoever. I am not being hypocritical here. I do maintain that physical closeness is more important, however, there should be some hint of mental compatibility. With The Twin I could see no mental connection. This girl used to act like a 10-year-old child. Whining about every little thing, acting like a little girl, saying please with an extra set of 'e's in the middle. I know most women are like that but I was done with immature women, for the time being at least.

I took The Twin around Boston and did everything I had already done with Shilpa. It was kind of a drag but I knew I would get some action in return so what the hell. I even took her on the famous Boston Duck Tours which I actually had never done before. Duck Tours are a tour of the historical town of Boston in vehicles used in World War 1 which can run on land and water. It is a great tour with the best part being when it enters the Charles River, one of the most beautiful rivers I have personally seen. Charles River is a beautiful sight in the winter when the whole river freezes and people actually ice skate on the river. Driving along the Charles River in winter is one of my favorite memories about Boston. Apart from the Duck Tour, I even took her to the Boston Aquarium. I had never been to the Boston Aquarium either, and it was a wonderful experience as well. It was nothing like the aquarium I had been to at San Francisco, but it was still a very nice aquarium. After a week of taking her around Boston, I had done pretty much everything a visitor would want to do in Boston. The next Monday we decided to stay at home at

Deshmukh's place. I went over and one thing led to another and soon I had reached fourth base. Again the whole physical experience with her never disappointed me. As a matter of fact, it was the best I had ever had up till that point.

We were in the middle of one of our raunchy sessions when something very funny happened. I decided to do it in my favorite position; doggy style*. I asked her to go on her knees which she did. I was finding my way about her posterior anatomy when suddenly she screamed, "Not in the ass!" I assured her I had no plans of doing anything of that sort. Why in the world would I have "unholy" intercourse without even asking her or talking to her about it? Wouldn't that constitute rape? Ass rape but rape nevertheless. I wanted to laugh at the whole thought of some guy inserting his penis into a girls anal rectum without telling her in advance. It would be like a couple having sex and suddenly the guy says, "Look honey a diamond ring". The girl looks up as goes, "Where? Where? I don't see....aaaaaaaargh my ass! You asshole!" That ain't cool man. Apart from that statement, it was a very satisfying experience and that was all we did after that day. After a whole week of the same, we decided to step out for a change. I was to meet her at her place by noon. However, I got caught up at the post office due to a very big line, and ended up about an hour late. Anyone who knows me knows that I hate to keep people waiting. I would never do it unless it was not in my control any more. One of my attributes that everyone will agree on is punctuality. In this case too, it was not in my control and unfortunately I reached her place an hour later than planned. The Twin just did not listen to my explanation. She gave me

*I don't have a dog so I can do that. Dog owners, as I have mentioned earlier, never do it!

the cold shoulder for almost an hour or so. She did not even say a word even when we were having lunch at *Au Bon Pain*. This really ticked me off. This girl was more immature than I had ever fathomed. I had to again go into my mode where the girl would get fed up of me and my antics, and dump me.

I love you is a strong statement which can freak out the best of us. But under two situations, it should never be taken seriously. One, when a guy/girl is drunk and second, when the guy/girl says it in the middle of being taken care of in bed, if you catch my drift. I had said those magical words to The Twin in both these situations and it had kind of working for me in the sense that she was feeling that I was coming on too strong. All I had to do now was to keep getting sentimental and soon she would run away. She was to leave for Pittsburgh soon and I went over to her brother's place the day before she was to leave. I was to help her pack, and also watch Father of the Bride with her as it was one of her favorite movies and I had never watched it before. We started the movie but I got bored. I started kissing her and soon we were in the bedroom. In the middle of it, she said the most romantic thing a girl could ever say to a guy. She said, "I might forget you, but I will never be able to forget this." This was followed by a chuckle of course. I knew the moment she said it she was not kidding. She was using the same trick I had been using since ages; say something serious and follow it with a smile and people will think you are joking. I had invented that trick! But I did not care if she was going to forget me. That is exactly what I wanted. We went on to do it 4 times before Father of the Bride ended, tying the record a friend of mine had set of doing it the same number of times during Castaway. However, with Castaway he got a good 3 hours while I got a little over an hour and a half so I suppose I beat his record. I kissed her goodbye knowing that it was definitely the last time I was going to see her. The next month my efforts were focused on coming up with as many corny dialogues as possible to drive The Twin into dumping my sorry ass. I was to visit my brother in Boulder again before the fall semester began and at the airport I was talking to her on the phone and I mentioned how much I missed her, in Hindi. In case you don't know, and my fellow Indians if you guys haven't noticed as yet, any dialogue sounds way more corny is Hindi. I don't know why but it just does and it is just the perfect weapon to drive the girl away. A week at Boulder, and I realized that The Twin was not returning my calls for days. And one day finally I got a huge email from her saying how it was hard for her to keep up with studies, and how she could not find time to talk to me which made her feel bad because she knew I was serious or whatever. She had rambled on and on. My reply to her was short and sweet; "Whatever you want."

The time I was in Boulder, I was also to move from my old apartment to a new one a bit away from school. It was still a 10-minute walk from school, but it meant walking through a park which was notorious for people getting mugged. My new roommates were Raj, a guy from Mumbai who was just too much in love with Mumbai but a great guy nevertheless and a lot of fun. Then there was J, a guy from Delhi who had done his undergrad in the US itself and liked to call himself J for because he thought that would make him cooler as he was far from anything you would call cool. Last but not least there was Mr. Bell, a guy who was Telugu but born and raised in Calcutta. Mr. Bell was a character alright but a nice guy at heart. As I was in Boulder, these guys were nice enough to volunteer to move my suitcases to the new apartment in J's car. I thought it was a very nice gesture and I was looking forward to living with my new roommates.

On reaching Boston, I realized I did not have the keys to the new house and called Raj to find out what I could do. He told me that Bell was home and that I could just call him and ask him to buzz me in. I took Bell's number and headed home. I did not have the key to the building either, and as Bell was not answering his phone, I decided to buzz my apartment number hoping that the noise would be enough to wake Bell up, assuming he was sleeping. However, buzzing didn't help either. Luckily for me, someone was coming out of the building which helped me get in. I started knocking on the door of my apartment but Bell just wasn't waking up. I was getting frustrated by now, and soon started kicking the door. After about 15-20 of creating a lot of noise, the door opened to a very drowsy looking Bell who said, "Oh you are back." As soon as I stepped in, someone knocked at the door. To my shock, it was the cops. Another non-paranoid American neighbor had called the police hearing all the noise thinking someone was trying to break into an apartment. I appreciate the concern, but wouldn't it just have been better to stick your head out and see what was happening? I am sure someone trying to break into an apartment will not come with a suitcase, a full one at that. I had to produce my ID and be questioned by the cops for a few minutes before being determined that I was in fact harmless. If only I knew who had called it in, I would have made it my mission in life to return the favor. I had also learned a new thing about one of our roommates. Even if someone was slowly torturing me to death without a gag, Bell would not hear it.

School soon started and I was back with my classmates whom I had taken most of previous classes with. Jon, an American, Gibran, a Pakistani, Lara (pronounced Laura) from Iceland, Ike Amazu, an American, Irem from Turkey and a couple of other Indians who loved to never do their homework and copy stuff from some of us whenever possible made up the people I hung out with in school. All these guys were really cool in their own way and I loved the fact that there was so much diversity in that group. Most of the Indians had a tendency to hang out with their own kind and it just didn't make sense to me. This fall semester also had something new about it. It was the first time I had started a semester single, and I had every intention of keeping it that way for some time. I did not want to go to the cool *desi* parties any more, and I did not know my undergrad friends well enough to hang out with them. My classmates were cool to hang out with for a few drinks, but they were not the kind to go out clubbing, apart from Lara who was a party animal but was strictly into black guys, though she did find me attractive which always was a boost to my confidence. With strictly limited options, I was left hanging out at home on weekends which made me want to kill myself. Then came my knight in shining armor, one of the very few good looking Indian guys at NU. His name was Chris, and he introduced me to the Boston nightlife.

.

Anecdote : Respect

Most of my anecdotes till now have been on the funnier side, or at least I have tried my best to make them funny. This time I would like to touch on a bit of a serious topic just because this particular incident pissed me off too much.

I recently stumbled upon a Facebook group created by Indian students from NU for the Diwali 2009 celebrations in school itself. Everyone was discussing how the event should be celebrated and how it can be made better. A Mr. Desai made a comment that really caught my attention. He had written, "It is ironic how Diwali coincides with Halloween, an American tradition where girls have a reason to dress up as sluts." This particular comment was followed by a lot of people saying that they loved what Mr. Desai had said. Let me tell you something Mr. Desai, you are a jackass, a big one at that. Let us see how many people love that comment of mine. How can you come to America and talk bad about their culture? You will never ever see an American come to India and diss our culture. One aspect about Americans which I respect is that they respect every tradition in this day and age. As a matter of fact, many visit India just to learn more about our culture. Who the hell are you Mr. Desai to say anything about the American culture? If you had any brains whatsoever, you would have looked up what Halloween is really about.

It is based on the ancient Celtic festival of Samhain. The festival of Samhain celebrates the end of the "lighter half" of the year and beginning of the "darker half", and is sometimes regarded as the "Celtic New Year". The ancient Celts believed that the border between this world and the Otherworld became thin on Samhain, allowing spirits (both harmless and harmful) to pass through. The family's ancestors were honored and invited home while harmful spirits were warded off. It is believed that the need to ward off harmful spirits led to the wearing of costumes and masks. I do agree that teenage girls dress slutty but just because a very small denomination of the population does that, does not mean the tradition is pathetic. You are pathetic for talking about someone's culture like that. Just because you don't get any sort of attention from these slutty girls, or girls in general*, does not mean you talk bad about them. Learn a thing or two about RESPECT Mr. Desai, you little prick.

---

*I have seen you picture Mr. Desai, and I am sure you don't get any attention from women, even those who barely pass as women.

In Da Club

Chris and I used to work together at the computer lab, and he told me how he used to go out every weekend diligently and how it wasn't too hard to find girls for good looking guys like us. At that point, I did consider myself a decent looking guy but never good looking. Though extremely skeptical about getting lucky with someone, I decided to give it a shot and went out with Chris one night.

This was not the first time I had gone out to a club in Boston. As I have mentioned earlier, I had gone to a club once in New York and then a couple of times in Boston with Shilpa and some other friends. The times I did go to these places with Shilpa were kind of exciting too because I did get some attention from women. The downside to going to a club with your girlfriend is that it takes out the whole thrill of hunting in a club which is the best part. It is literally a jungle out there. Chris and I reached the club, Caprice, around 11:30pm which gave us a good 2 and a half hours to hunt. By midnight the place was pretty full with a lot of good-looking women. Chris told me that hunting in a pack never really worked much, though having a wingman always helped if there were only two women. He also told me that if there are a group of girls dancing, it would be next to impossible to approach one of them and pull them away. Learning these new tactics took me some time but after a couple of more tips, we split ways to hunt alone and it was time for me to use all the newly acquired knowledge. I stood there, sipping on my Red Bull as Chris had warned me that having too much to drink might affect my performance if I were to get lucky later on. Instead of approaching someone, I tried this thing of just looking at any girl who looked good and seemed single. Not staring but just giving glances to show that I was interested in them. The reason in doing this and not being more proactive was that men have to come up with something extremely clever or extremely funny when approaching a girl or else she will not be interested in you. On the other hand, all the girl has to do is come up to a guy and say 'hi' and she is in, mostly because men are just that horny*. Thinking on those lines, I waited there looking at a few girls and soon I had a girl come over and talk to me. After buying her a drink, we decided to hit the dance floor. Now this was going to be the hard part because this is not the crazy dance we Indians do on the streets during festivals. A good dancer makes a very good impression on a woman and I was far from being a good dancer. However, thankfully, all this girl wanted to do was grind with me. By the end of the night, I was a very happy man and nothing in the world could have wiped the grin on my face at that moment. Chris too had been lucky to find an attractive woman, but then again he was an experienced guy so he getting with a girl didn't really surprise me much. My first time in the club was amazing and I wanted more. It soon became an addiction of sorts.

Apart from clubbing, Northeastern was a good place to meet new women too. I was single and the whole Indian community knew it after a much publicized break up with Shilpa. I always believed that the *FOB* (Fresh of the boat)

And then women complain about equal rights. Look at how hard life is for us men!

Indian girls checked me out even when I was with Shilpa but I always convinced myself that it was because I was with a good looking girl and women in general have a tendency to check out guys who are not single. But now that I was, I started getting some attention. The fall 2007 batch had got in some new girls, none good looking as such but girls who would not be bad to take all the pressure off my right hand. One of them was Ms. Gupte who had done her undergrad from Ohio State and now was enrolled in the masters program at NU. One day while coming back after my shift at the computer lab, I saw my friends helping some new people move in, out of which Ms. Gupte was one of them. Though not the kind of just take your breath away at the first look, she was the only one who was dressed well which does catch your attention. But more than her catching my attention, it was the other way around and she kept looking at me. Liking the glares from her, I stood around there talking to my friends, and to people I barely knew just so that she got a good look at me. I also found out her name through someone. The next day, while working at the computer lab, I was handing out printouts when I noticed a printout with her name. I pushed it to the end of the pile so that when she came up she would keep waiting giving her more opportunity to stare at me, and for me to act cool. At the end, I held her printout and saw that it was her resume. I looked at her and asked her if it was her printout and she replied affirmatively. To just start some conversation, I started glancing through her resume saying, "Let me see what you have been up to." She laughed and snatched her resume off my hand. This was enough for me to talk to her for a bit and add her on Facebook. Soon enough we sent out a few messages to each other via Facebook and she told me she wanted to go out clubbing and would like me to come. I was more than happy to accept her request. Now all that was left to do was to make sure I had a wingman because she was going to call a couple of girls too. And who better to call than my closest friend Rehan?

Rehan had broken up with Soniya and was looking for something to keep his mind occupied. I asked him to come over to Boston, with Mary of course, so that we could go out with Ms. Gupte and her friends. That weekend itself Rehan came over and I made plans to go out to a club. We met up with Ms. Gupte and her friends there. We were already stoned and Rehan continued to get me drinks. After a while, I saw Rehan dancing really close to one of Ms. Gupte's friends, and by close I mean really freaking close. This got me to ask my girl for the night to dance with me and she obliged. Grinding with a girl is always fun, but it is even more fun when you know you are going back to the girl's place at the end of the night. All of us headed back to Ms. Gupte's house, and I got the couch along with her while a couple of her friends from New York got the bed. Rehan and the girl he was dancing with had gone missing from the house so I knew what was happening there. After her friend's from New York had slept off, I asked Gupte if she wanted to grab something to eat. After grabbing a couple of slices of pizza, we reached her building. While she was taking out her keys, I decided to make my move. As I went in to kiss her, she pulled away saying this could be a bit complicated. When I asked the reason, she told me she had a boyfriend in California. Though she had a boyfriend, she used the words "it could be complicated" and not "I have a boyfriend. Go away!" This obviously meant she didn't mind it but just wanted to put it out there that she was seeing someone and so was not looking for something serious, which was even more perfect for me. After she had said that, I just looked at her and smiled, and said, "Don't worry, I like complications." and kissed her. I headed home the next morning, with Rehan who had sneaked into the house sometime in the night, and both of us had a smile on our faces.

I did not call Ms. Gupte much, and she did not call me either. I would get a call once in a while from her asking me if I would like to come over because she had some friends over which I would usually decline just because I would be busy with something or the other. But one night, my roommate Raj and I were having a few drinks and ran out of alcohol. The wine shops were closed by then and we were pondering over what to do when I got a call from Gupte. She as usual had some friends over and wanted me to join them. I dragged Raj along and went over. One of Gupte's female friends, Bipasha, seemed very interesting to me. Again, she was not really good looking but had great hair which I always respect. Apart from that, she was really great to talk to and was a very interesting person in general. I spend the whole night talking to her which got Gupte very jealous.

Raj left for home in a while and so did her other friends which left only me, Gupte and Bipasha. Gupte really wanted me to join her in the bedroom but I was just not interested because I was too intrigued by this new girl. Ms. Gupte eventually gave up and went in to sleep. But while continuing to talk to Bipasha, Gupte suddenly came out of the bedroom and just sat in my lap for a while. I had to take a leak and I went into the restroom, also hoping that Gupte would sleep by then or at least leave me alone with Bipasha. While I was peeing, someone started knocking on the door. I hurried up and opened the door only to have Gupte push me back in. She came into the restroom with me and locked the door. By this time I was a bit drunk and so decided to just go along with it. We were in the toilet for a good ten minutes when she suddenly stopped and said, "You have to go out and tell Bipasha you are sleeping on the bed with me and then come into the bedroom if you want to go all the way with me tonight." This kind of pissed me off a bit. I got out of the restroom and just sat there with Bipasha, again making conversation. Gupte soon asked me to come out with her for a smoke. While outside she made it very clear to me that I should stop flirting with her friend. She told me I could flirt with anyone I wanted but not her friends, which is in fact a very fair thing to say but considering I was a bit ticked off I just told her that since I was single I could flirt with anyone.

Gupte tried her level best to convince me but to no avail. In the end she said, "I can't believe an Indian guy from Northeastern is rejecting me." This from a girl who only had a good dressing sense going for her and a nose ring of course which is a big turn on for some reason for me*. I know Indian guys at NU can be a pretty uncouth bunch but some of them were great people and my friends. And most of all, she was talking about me, a guy whom she should consider lucky to have gotten the opportunity to spend some quality time with. I was in fact so out of her league, that she should be telling her

*Sonakshi Sinha take note.

grandchildren about the time she was with Anish. Though I was pissed off, it was raining and I did not want to be thrown out of the house at that time. I just told her that I would like the freedom to flirt with anyone and that she was not giving me that opportunity. Though ticked off, she was nice enough to let me stay for the night and leave early morning. As she went off to sleep, I started my conversation again with Bipasha in the hopes of getting some from there too.

We spoke for a couple of hours and then she said she was going to crash. As she had the couch, I decided to rest on a nice comfortable chair next to it. Sometime in the night, I heard some noise and woke up. It was Bipasha just getting up to go to the restroom. In the process, she had one of those wardrobe malfunctions! She was sleepy and so slowly corrected the slip of the dress by pulling it up. This coupled with the fact that I had just been in the toilet with another girl just a couple of hours back, turned me on. I had to do something. I could not let her go back to sleep. As she came back, I started some conversation in an effort to keep her awake. I even got up and sat next to her on the couch. Within 5 minutes, I made my move. I held her hand and kissed it. She did not say anything or move away. Then I just leaned in and kissed her. We decided we should stop as daylight was already creeping into the house which meant Ms. Gupte could get up at any point. We decided to grab breakfast and go watch Bourne Ultimatum just so that we could continue where we left off in the theatre. During breakfast, she told me that she was a virgin and that she had never even been touched down there because she was afraid it might hurt her. Apparently, she preferred her posterior rectum being touched or taken care of. How is that any less painful? I do understand that there are a lot of nerve endings in the anus but if you are looking for less pain shouldn't that be the one area you should always veer away from? She even said that she would like her first sexual experience to be the unholy kind as well. Whoever said Indian women are not freaky in bed? Hey I always wanted to try this so why would I say no? I went ahead to the theatre with a lot of curiosity.

Though I knew I was not going to go all the way in the theatre, I could not wait to get to the theatre. I had already seen the movie which is why I selected that. Under no circumstances would I otherwise disrespect Jason Bourne. As the movie started, I helped her to be happy in whatever way she wanted me to make her happy. Though she did not return the favor, I could not stop smiling as we made a beeline for the exit. We made plans to meet up at my place the next day. I made sure my roommates knew that I was going to be with a girl at home and also made sure I would at least get a couple of hours alone with her. Mr. Bell was all cranky but in the end I literally pushed him out of the house. Bipasha soon came over and we spoke for a while before we were at it again. This time again the trend continued with me being the giver and her only receiving. I am usually the giver and I actually enjoy satisfying a woman. However, I am no Mother Teresa to only give and never take. By the end of that little rendezvous at my place, I was a bit frustrated and that was enough for me to push Bipasha out of my life.

Chris and I continued our weekly clubbing and we were really enjoying ourselves. I met a lot of women of different nationalities. However, Indian women born and raised in the

US, the so-called *ABCD*s, (American Born Confused Desi) were the funniest. The first question I usually got when I approached an Indian girl, or if they approached me, would be, "Are you Hindu?" Why would anyone ask someone's religion in a club? It is not like I am going to marry a girl whom I met in a club. I am not saying that people who enjoy the nightlife are not good or anything like that. It is just that when my kids ask me about how I met their mother, I don't want my answer to be, "Well children I was drunk and horny and your mom was the only one I got. The next morning our Indian values kicked in and we decided to get married." Though it sounds like a typical Bollywood movie scene where the main characters have to get married to rectify their "mistake", I would not want to be the one saying that story to my kids. Whenever some girl asked me that question, being the slut that I am, I would just reply with a smile, "I can be whatever you want me to be."

Another thing about these *ABCD* (American Born Confused Desi) girls was that as soon as they learned that I was a graduate student, they would be a put off. Usually Indian graduate students are *FOB*s (Fresh of the boat) and these girls hate our kind. I think they believe we are not refined enough for them, or maybe they just think we are too horny. I have a news flash for you my dear American born Indians; All men are horny! Let me give you an example of how men are hornier than women. Have you seen ads for Pepsi or Coke? When an extremely hot and sweaty woman is drinking Pepsi or Coke, I feel like having that drink. It automatically makes me thirsty and makes me crave that drink. I might have been fooled earlier by Cindy Crawford, or Aishwarya Rai in her first ever ad, but every time I see a new girl drink the same drink, I feel like having the same thing all over again. Maybe this new girl is drinking Pepsi now because they changed it somehow from when Cindy or Ash were having it. Women on the other hand are not really affected by a hot guy drinking cola. They look at the guy, think he is hot, and move on. So my dear brothers and sisters from another mother do not just think of us PIGS as horny. It is just in our genes and there is nothing we can do to change it.

Chris and I continued our escapades in clubs every weekend. Studies seemed much less a priority as compared to going out on weekends. I would spend all week just dreaming of whom I might meet the coming weekend. One fine Saturday night, we went out to a club but were disappointed with the crowd. After an hour or so, we left the place is search of greener pastures. As soon as we stepped out, we met a couple of older women whom Chris knew, and they were Russian! We asked them to join us and went to a club called Gypsy Bar. After a couple of drinks I started dancing with my Russian lady, whose name I do not remember. She touched my arms while dancing and asked me if I worked out. I am not really jacked but if a woman asks you as question like that you do not say no. She was somehow impressed and a few minutes later kissed me. After a while, all four of us decided to bounce and go back to my lady's house. However, Chris' lady bailed on us as a result of which he left too. I went over to my lady's house to finish what I had started. She popped open a bottle of champagne and we were sitting on her couch and joking around. She asked me to keep it a bit down as her son was sleeping in the other room. I was taken aback for a second. Then it finally sunk in. I was with a Russian MILF! I consider myself an atheist but from that moment onwards, I was ready to turn into a believer. The Gods had made a couple of my biggest dreams come true. She was Russian, and she was a mother. God is great. But my excitement was short lived. I asked her how old her son was to which she replied, "14." 14! If a 14 year old kid were to walk in on his mother having sex with a 24 year old, he would be scarred for life, and I most definitely did not want to be the reason for such a traumatic experience in anyone's life. But how could I give up an opportunity with a Russian MILF?

I had a couple more glasses of champagne to muster some courage. She asked me if I wanted to move into her room to which I happily obliged. While we were in the middle of non-reproductive intercourse, it was really tough for me to ignore the fact that she had a 14-year-old son who might wake up and catch us in the act. To make it harder for me to concentrate, she said, "When I close my eyes, it feels like I am with a man. When I open them, I see a boy." What the hell does that mean? Well I suppose that is better than looking like a man and feeling like a boy. Both of us were tired by the end of it, and decided to take a quick nap before she offered to drop me home. This was amazing. Not only does she take me back to her place, she even drops me home. This takes out one of the biggest problems for us PIGS. If one of us has to take a girl back home, we have to call up our 6-8 roommates and ask them to get out of the house. Considering that most of them have never had sex in their life, they would all either hang around in the adjoining room, or somewhere close to the building so they can take a good look at the girl. After getting the girl over, if the girl is screaming during the act, it does not necessarily mean that she is enjoying it. It could also be that the bed bugs are biting her. Bed bugs are not really a testament of poor living conditions as a lot of people think. It is just that some cities have a problem with these bugs and it takes an effort from the building management, and the tenants to eradicate these bugs. Coming back to topic, after putting her through that painful experience, you would not want the girl to go home alone at night. As a student, very few of us graduate students have cars and as result of which you will end up spending quite a bit of money on cabs to drop the girl home and come back. Considering all this, a single working woman seemed a way better option.

You would think that all these extra-curricular activities would definitely screw up my grades but I guess I am a jack-of-all-trades. I was doing well in that semester, and was on course for a couple of A minus' at least if not straight As. I was also enjoying my football. Life was going great. However, one thing really upset me. All of batch mates, people who had come in to NU in fall 2006, were going back in Dec 2007 to meet their family and friends. All of them had saved money from their internships, or from their on campus jobs to buy their own tickets. I on the other hand had not thought of saving any money at all. I was living on a strict hand to mouth basis, and the little I saved would be spent in clubs every weekend. I could have asked my folks to pay for my tickets but it just seemed wrong on my part to ask them for it as they were already spending a fortune in my tuition fees at NU. Though I was not big on going back within one and a half years of getting to the US, I definitely did miss my family and friends but I had to wait till I could afford my own ticket.

Though Rehan had broken up with Soniya, they kept trying to make it work. This involved him travelling a lot from New Jersey to California whenever he could so that they could spend more time together. However, every time he went there, they would somehow end up fighting. And when he was back in New Jersey, they would talk everyday like nothing had happened. It was very confusing, and I was in a tough spot because I knew and spoke to both of them. My loyalties of course lay with Rehan, though I had become very close friends with Soniya as well. We would chat pretty often online, and even call each other. If they had any problems I would try my level best to sort things out between them. I would try to make Rehan understand how Soniya is a nice girl, and she deserves him to listen to her more and understand her more. Rehan on the other hand kept telling me how I don't know Soniya like he does and that she is completely childish and kind of psychotic. I always laughed at it whenever he said something like that. I wish I knew those very things would come back to bite me in the butt.

Coming back to enjoying the nightlife, it had reached a point where even if I did not have any company, I would go out. It was more than an addiction; it became an obsession. Usually, when I was alone, I would go to Caprice as it had always been a happy hunting ground for me. But one day, I decided to change it a bit and go to Gypsy Bar just because I was getting tired of the former place. It seemed like it was going to be an uneventful night with only a few not so good looking Indian women giving me looks. But like in the movies, the crowd separated, and in the middle there was a girl dancing with her friend, and she was totally checking me out. This girl looked European and that was a plus point in its own. Gradually, they started dancing closer and closer to me. I knew what was happening but I still did not make a move; I did not want to unless I was completely sure. A few minutes later, her friend pushed this girl onto me while dancing. I would be a fool to not take this opportunity but I didn't. I waited. Other guys soon noticed the 2 single women and started hitting on them. One guy was particularly persistent and kept hitting on my girl though she refused a million times. When he tried again, like a knight in shining armor, I went close to her and held out my hand. She looked at me and smiled, a smile which said, "What the hell took you so long?" As soon as she came close to me, we started dancing really close. We continued that till the club shut and we stood outside. Her name was Maida, and was originally from Slovakia though she now resided in Vermont. She was visiting her friend in Boston and was also planning to move to Boston. She gave me her number and told me to call her the next day. On asking her why she was not taking me back to her place, she told me that if I met her for lunch she would take me home some time soon. Sometime soon was not good for me, and as soon as she left I deleted her number. Of course I did that in my drunken state. How I regret that moment.

I ran into this Indian girl at the club Caprice once, whose name was either Shweta or Shruti. For the sake of convenience, I will call her Shruti. Shruti kept looking at me the whole night but as she was not that attractive, I kept her as a last option. In the end I did have to fall onto my last option and dance with her. While dancing she told me that I was a good dancer. If anyone thought I was a good dancer, they had a serious problem with their eyesight, or they had to be retarded. We stayed till the end and got a cab together. I really wanted to go back to her place. In an attempt to enter her house, I asked her if I could use the restroom at her place as I really needed to go. She happily welcomed me to her home. After using the restroom, I decided to move things along but she backed away as I leaned in to kiss her. She told me that she had never done this before and that she wanted to talk to me a bit and know me better before anything happened. So in order to do that, she started telling me her story, and how she was recently divorced and that her husband was someone who always listened to his mother. Shruti was an intern doctor in Boston which definitely made me respect her a bit. But then she lost all that respect when she started showing me her family photos with her sister, mom and dad. How long was this going to take? After finally finishing the album, we went for it. However, just like Allie, this girl was not kissing me either. It was not like she was seeing someone or married, but I suppose she was still not over her ex-husband. I guess it is an Indian woman thing to go all the way but not kiss a guy so that you don't feel guilty about it. We soon slept for a bit, and I got up as soon as there was a bit of sunlight. She walked me down to the front door of the building. I was happy that she was not bothering me with her number or anything and was just about to get out of the building when she suddenly started laughing.

It was a very sarcastic laughter of sorts. The kind that would make you ask her what happened. On questioning her, she said, "You didn't take my number." I quickly started rummaging through my phone number saying," I thought I took it last night." though I was sure I did not have her number. Pretending to be disappointed, I asked her for her number to which she said, "Now if you need my number, you will have to stand outside my house every day for the next 3 days." I laughed and said I will definitely do that and left, never to return to that neighborhood again.

Rehan's relationship with Soniya had finally hit rock bottom. They had ended their relationship but were still friends. It never works out like that and they constantly had fights. I was the mediator again and in the process would end up talking to Soniya a lot. I had been talking to this girl for over 3 years now but had never met her. It was surprising that I was such good friends with a girl whom I had never met before. Of course, the fact that she was at one point dating my best friend had a lot to do with it but still it was a bit surprising. Soniya and I started talking a lot over the phone. So much so that I would end up talking to her more over the course of a week than I would with Rehan. Though she was still in talking terms with Rehan, she definitely started sharing more with me. My friends Bhatia and Patil started asking me if I was dating Soniya. I would laugh at the very idea of me dating Soniya. She was not my best friend's girlfriend anymore but still the idea of dating your closest friend's ex-girlfriend seems weird. And of course it is a golden rule that you do not mess with your friends' ex-girlfriends or sisters or anyone related to your friends. However, my friends constantly nagged me regarding Soniya. Has it ever happened to you that someone keeps making fun of you or teasing you with some girl and inadvertently you start wondering if there is in fact something going on? This happened to me, and I started wondering if there was anything going on between us. I definitely would look forward to talk to Soniya each day, and she would call me too for the smallest of things like asking me to double check an answer she just wrote in a test, on the web. There was definitely something going on but there was no way in hell I could do that to Rehan. One day Soniya told me that she was come to visit her friend in New Jersey City, an hour's drive from Rehan's house, and that I should stay with Rehan for a couple of weeks till she was there so we could meet pretty much every day. I was excited that she was coming so that I could finally meet the girl I was talking to since so many years. But at the same time I was afraid that something might happen between us which would be so wrong. I decided to go ahead and meet Soniya. I just hoped that nothing bad would happen.

Anecdote : Milf Hunter

There was an article on Om Puri which mentioned his sexual relationships with his maid when he was a young boy of around 14. Mr. Puri you are a great actor, one of the best in Bollywood, and I really respect you. You never denied these stories, but said that you were annoyed at your wife for writing these intimate stories in her book. You went on to say that it was a beautiful relationship you had with this maid and that it was sacred. Sir, with all due respect, and I say with all due respect, but there is nothing sacred about doing it with your maid. Every guy has a tendency to hit on their maids in India and a few get lucky as well. But calling the whole thing sacred was a bit disturbing. But what was most disturbing about reading about this whole ordeal was that I actually had nude images of Om Puri in my head and let me tell you my friends that it was not good. I have officially been scarred for life by Om Puri.

Hoes before Bros : part 2

I took the bus from the Boston Chinatown which took me to New York. From there, I had to catch a train. Finally, after travelling for around 6 hours, I reached the train stop where Rehan and Soniya were supposed to pick me up. Rehan told me that they were stuck in traffic, and that it would be a while before they reached. Considering it was December, the temperatures were low enough to make me shiver, and to freeze my brain enough to not think of waiting inside the heated waiting room. Though I had my jacket on, it was still cold and I could not take it much longer. Even the large cup of hot chocolate I had bought from Dunkin Doughnuts was getting over. Just when I thought I might soon be categorized as a cold-blooded creature, I saw Rehan pulling in. Though I was pissed off, I did not show it as I was really excited to meet Soniya. From all the pictures I had seen of her on Facebook, Soniya was an attractive girl. However, that was the day I realized how deceptive pictures can be, and also how well Photoshop works. Though Soniya looked alright, she looked like an imposter to me; a girl who was a look alike even of the girl on Facebook, a not-so-good-looking look alike but one nevertheless. However, I did not care about it that much because I was not going to date this girl or something, and I had a great connection with her. She was one of my closest friends and I was just happy to meet her.

We drove back to Rehan's place where Soniya gave us some sweaters she had got for us. I absolutely loved my sweater and could not wait to wear it when we went out. After talking for a while, Rehan and I met Mary while Soniya gave us company. We decided to go get some Indian rolls in New York the following evening where Soniya and her friend she was staying with, Rita, were supposed to meet some high school friends. Rehan and I had decided that before doing anything on that trip, we would meet Mary and it was the best idea we could have come up with. Their school friends were the most annoying bunch of people I had ever met, who were still obsessed about gossiping about their school-mates. I had noticed the previous night that when Soniya and Rita were together, they would do the same too. They would log on to Facebook or Orkut, and check profiles of their schoolmates and bitch about how bad they looked or how annoying they were back in the day. They would even go to the extent of calling pretty much everyone lame. I guess everyone from their high school were lame considering these two were actually doing this 3-4 years after coming out of the school and after moving to a whole new country. Again, I did not look much into it as I did not want to think anything negative about Soniya. While eating the delicious rolls, one of her school friends asked me if I was dating Soniya. I was taken aback, and caught off guard. I stumbled a bit before blurting out a very emphatic "No". My response was very suspicious, and even Rehan gave me a look which pretty much said, "What the f**k was that?" I ignored it and started some random conversation which I think made Rehan all the more suspicious. After everyone left that place, we decided to hit a bar. The school gang wanted to go to some bar which was about 30 blocks away, while there was a good enough bar 30 feet away. We asked them to go ahead and told them that we would meet them. However, we ditched them and went to the bar which was closer. After a few drinks, Rehan and I went out for a smoke where out of the blue he told me that he and Soniya were late to pick me up because they had taken a room in some hotel. I was pretty taken aback by this revelation. I asked him if they were back together but he dismissed that with a chuckle saying that it was just breakup sex. I could feel a knot in my stomach right then. Him telling me that just put images in my head which I would have never wanted to have. To get them out, I decided to drink more.

A few drinks later, all the images were gone and I was relaxed once again. In fact, I became so relaxed that I held Soniya's hand and put it inside my t-shirt to make her feel my non-existent abs. I was cautious enough to do it when Rehan was not around, however, Rita and her fiancé gave Soniya the same look Rehan had given me a few hours back. All through the night, Rehan seemed distant and I had a feeling it had a lot to do with the chemistry between me and Soniya. On our way back, he had a fight with Soniya though he did not really specify what he was angry about. We drove in silence till we got to Rita's house. I offered to drop Soniya upstairs as it was late in the night and Rehan was definitely not in a courteous mood. On our way up to Rita's apartment, Soniya started crying thinking about the fight she just had with Rehan. I did not want to interfere. However, I definitely wanted to console her. I held her close and didn't let her go till she had calmed down. Somehow holding her in my arms felt really good. Once I let her go, we decided that we would not cancel our plans to go to the club called Tonic in New York the next day because of a stupid fight. Tonic has Indian nights on Saturdays and they play only Bollywood music. This wouldn't be the first time for me, or Rehan, at Tonic. Whenever I visited him in New Jersey, we would go to Tonic just because we believed Indian girls were easier for us to pick up. But once again the problem would be the guys who came to the club with the girls who would protect the girls from "evil". Once I was dancing with this really cute girl, the only one I had ever seen at Tonic. After a while, her friend, a guy, comes over and says, "Enough!" What do you mean enough? I want more! But of course she left and I was left standing there, wondering what the hell just happened. Tonic was, and still is, the worst club to pick up girls. We really have no idea why we always went there.

The following night, just before we were to leave for Rita's house, Rehan and I decided to meet Mary to enhance the experience of the 1-hour drive. We set off happy and were soon having a blast on the road. Halfway through the journey, for some unknown and unexplainable reason, I felt like hitting Rehan, in a friendly way of course. I started hitting him like how girls hit each other in a catfight. Now considering he was driving, I really did not expect him to retaliate in any way. But the *Veer** that he was, he could not resist a fight. He left the wheel and started hitting me back. All this was happening on a highway while we were travelling at about 80-100 mph. and suddenly someone's hand hit the steering wheel and the car was out of control. Rehan tried his level best to stabilize it but to no avail. The car took a 180-degree turn and halted facing the oncoming traffic. Luckily for us, the cars behind us were

*Veer = Brave in Hindi. It is also a Bollywood movie starring Salman Khan; a movie so bad that even 3/4th bottle of rum could not help us in enjoying it.

maybe about 30 seconds away. Rehan turned the wheel as quickly as possible and floored the accelerator for us to get going in the right direction again. I could see the bright headlights of a couple of cars right on our tail through the side-view mirror, and the 'Objects in the mirror might be closer than they appear' sign did not help my nerves in any which way. Rehan floored the gas once again and soon we were within safe distance from the cars behind. I could not utter a single word till we got to Rita's place. Talk about buzz kills. Soniya started laughing the minute we walked into Rita's apartment. Rehan and I were wearing the t-shirts/sweaters that she had given us. And to top it off, both were pretty similar. In the meanwhile, I was checking out Soniya and how attractive she was looking. I knew make-up could do wonders but this was a staggering transformation. If I ever become even remotely famous, I will make sure to promote the brand(s) she was using. She was wearing a black dress which though showed off her "curvy" body, looked good on her. I had to refrain myself from staring at her, and soon we were off to Tonic. After we got in, Rehan and I went out again to meet Mary once again considering the whole high from the drive had been ruined by our little catfight. We made our way back through the bunch of desperate looking Indian men and manly looking Indian women to where the rest of our group was. Tonic has a wall on which all the single guys wanting to hook up would lean against with a drink in their hand. All of us were laughing at those guys when we realized that one of our friends was in the midst of the desperados as well. Soon enough we were all drunk enough and started shaking our booties to the Bollywood numbers. Rita for some reason was dancing close to me in spite of her fiancé being around. Any guy who is drunk, and in a club environment, would get a little excited with a decent enough girl dancing close to him. So I reciprocated and we were pretty close to each other. However, Soniya quickly pulled me away and told me that Rita's fiancé was getting pissed off. I really didn't know how it was my fault. I was single after all. Anyway, I told Soniya that since she had dragged me aside, she would have to find me a girl to dance with. So we took a walk around the dance floor to find a good-looking girl but to no avail. Finally we gave u and decided to sit on a couch which was on the other side of the dance floor to where our friends were, including Rehan. We were pretty exhausted, and Soniya rested her head against my shoulder. Suddenly, Soniya looked up at me and me down at her. Our eyes were locked for a second before she leaned in and kissed me. I was kissing my best friend's ex-girlfriend! This was definitely not right.

I had feelings for this girl but kissing your friend's ex-girlfriend or sister is just against the rules. Quickly, I pulled away and looked at her not knowing what to say. But my feelings for her just took over my sense of right and wrong and I kissed her again, and this time neither of us pulled away. I held her hand to tell her it was going to be ok and that it was going to work out. We walked back to our friends and danced the night away. As soon as we got out of the club, Rehan seemed a bit uneasy. He started asking us where we had vanished for a while, and what we were doing in that time. Though our answers were convincing enough, it did not seem like he was buying it. He knew something fishy was going on and so he asked Soniya if she liked me. She said 'yes'. I was shocked. How could she do that? I had to break it to him some other way. Not like this when we were outside a club and intoxicated. He then asked me if I liked her to which I replied, "Yes but only as a friend." Though Soniya was offended by my reply, I was sure she would understand why I did that.

Over the course of the next one-week that we met up before Soniya had to leave, we would take every opportunity to spend some time alone with each other. Not just to kiss each other or have any sort of physical contact, but also to just talk. A few nights Soniya spent at Rehan's with us, we would sit up and talk all night after Rehan fell asleep. It felt great to date one of my close friends. It was like Monica and Chandler hooking up in Friends. But at the same time, it was also like Joey and Rachel hooking up considering the Ross factor. Knowing her for so long before anything happened between us made me feel like there were no pretenses which are usually existent during the start of a relationship, or anything close to a relationship. Soon enough it was time for her to leave, and Rehan and I dropped her to the airport. Saying goodbye to her was the toughest thing I had ever done. I could not hold her in my arms long enough because Rehan was around, and I did not know when we would meet next as she was off to LA and I was going back to Boston. However, I was determined to meet her again and make this work out somehow. I definitely had a good feeling about this. The only problem was breaking it to Rehan.

A couple of days after Soniya left, I left for Boston too. By the time I got back, the spring 2008 semester had started. I was trying for an internship for a long time and finally got a shot at an interview. The company was called Radiant and was located in New Hampshire, a two-hour trip by road. I went there for an interview and was soon accepted by the company as an intern. I could have moved to New Hampshire which would negate the 4 hours of travelling every day. However, it was a bigger pain to find someone to sublet the room, and considering my roommates, no one would want to move in there even for 6 months. So travelling it was. In the meanwhile, Soniya and I would talk every day on the phone, as well as webcam whenever possible. It was going great but every time after I was done talking to her, I would feel guilty and would immediately call Rehan to talk to him for a bit. I just didn't know how I could tell this to him. He was going through a bad patch in his life where his H1B Visa approval was getting postponed as a result of which he could not work either. I did not want to pile on the bad news and so decided to wait till he was a bit settled to break it to him. One night, after I was asleep, I got a call from Rehan. I ignored it because I was really sleepy. However, he kept calling and finally I picked up on his fourth attempt. As soon as I picked up, I realized he was crying. He started asking me how I could do this to him and how I was just being another Crassy. Though I hated being compared with Crassy the douchebag, I knew he was right. Soniya had told him about us which ticked me off. I had told her a million times that I will tell it to him but she just went ahead with it anyway. I was royally pissed but at the moment I had to focus on making my friend feel fine. He did not listen to anything I said, and finally hung up saying he never wanted to see me or talk to me again. I had just lost my closest friend.

Not talking to Rehan was definitely bad. We would talk about anything and everything, and now he was not around anymore. I wanted to tell Soniya how much I hated her for telling him but then again I wanted to try make this work so I just kept quiet. I went on with my life of travelling to New Hampshire and back every day. It was a very hectic routine. I would get up by 6:30am, leave the house by 8:00am, get the bus from South Station at 8:45 which left me close to work at around 10:00am, work till 5:50pm and run to catch the bus at 6:00pm, get back to Boston by 7:00pm then hit the Northeastern gym before getting back home by 8:30pm give or take a few minutes. It was a routine I was getting used to. I enjoyed myself at Radiant though it was not really the most interesting of works. There was a client manager Alice who had joined a week before me. All Alice did all day was watch her adopted dog in the webcam provided by the doggy day care where she left her pooch when she came for work. I was surprised that I knew more than her about the system we were working on, and yet I was an intern while she was a client manager. A few weeks later a new intern was being interviewed and I was given the task of explaining our software to him, and to see if he was good enough to work with our team. I was really excited as within a few weeks of working there, I was a part of the interviewing process, a small part, but a part nevertheless.

The day of the interview I was all excited to meet and interview a potential colleague. And soon enough, in walked Greg Lonsdale. At first glance, I was disappointed looking at Greg. He was what would be classified as a geek if you were to go just by his looks. He wore a blue shirt tucked into his light brown pants, and wore jogging shoes. He had glasses too to complete the geeky look. Though I was very skeptical about working with such a guy for about 6 months, he definitely seemed up for the task and seemed very interested in working there. So he was soon on board the Radiant Client Management team. He would sit right next to me and we would talk all day long. I was completely taken aback by this guy. He was really cool, with a good sense of humor, and was intelligent too in a non-geeky kind of way. I was glad he was there and it definitely meant me not getting bored at work. Also, Fridays meant company lunch for which Greg and I would always be more than prepared. We would mostly skip breakfast so that we could feast on the good food set in the cafeteria. As soon as the clock struck noon, we would take turns to see if the food had arrived. We would always be one of the first ones there, and would always take food as if we had not eaten for ages. All in all, I was having a blast at Radiant. However, to every upside there is a flipside. And my flipside was Soniya.

Soniya and I were actually very compatible. In fact, I was surprised at how compatible we were. We could actually figure out what the other person was thinking, or what the other person was going to do without any exchange of words. It was marvelous. However, unfortunately, she also knew all the details about my relationship with Shilpa. It had been close to a year and a half since my relationship with Shilpa had ended but Soniya had an inkling that I was not over Shilpa. Soniya was so insecure that at times I would feel that she was more into Shilpa than I ever was. One day I put up a picture, which was originally taken with Shilpa by my side, on Facebook as my profile picture. Since the breakup, I had cut off Shilpa from the picture and so had just me in it. But Soniya being the ever so insecure person gave me hell for putting that up. She called me and started off the conversation by saying, "You don't respect me do you?" And I am wondering what in the world is going on. She continued saying, "The whole world knows that this photo was taken with Shilpa. They will think you don't respect me and that is why you have that picture up." I cut the woman off that picture! What more could I do? Considering I am the least photogenic person in the world, this was one of the very few pictures I had in which I look presentable. But Soniya started crying over the phone saying a bit of Shilpa's arm could still be seen in it. I had to literally use a magnifying glass to see that, so forget about the world. This woman was insane. But I had made a big commitment here. I had crossed my friend because I thought it was worth it. Now his warning about her being a psycho was coming forth. What do I do now?

I gave Soniya some benefit of doubt for her psychotic behavior. I told myself that the distance between us was causing all the trouble. So I decided to go to Pasadena, Los Angeles to stay at her place while she was alone at home for a week. It was a long weekend so I just had to take a day off at work so that I got 4 days in LA. I landed at LAX airport around 10:00pm where I was greeted by an excited Soniya. We went back to her place and slept early as we had planned to roam around Pasadena a bit the following day. The next day was fun as we did a lot of touristy things and were out for pretty much the entire day. After getting back home, we decided to have a couple of glasses of wine. The wine gave us a nice buzz and soon enough we were in more than a romantic mood. In the middle of our physical exploits, something really strange happened. While I was pleasuring her, Soniya called me 'Daddy'. I know very well that women tend to call their men 'Big Daddy' or something to that effect but you really need to understand the importance of the word 'Big' there. Not only did she call me that, she said that like an eight year old would say it. I am not saying it was the Oedipus effect or something but I was completely shocked, and turned off of course. I pretended to be extremely tired and slept off, with very disturbing thoughts.

The next few days in the city of angels were a blur. I just could not focus on anything since I had heard those words from Soniya's mouth. Though I had to engage in physical activities with her to show that I was content in the relationship, it had me faking it a lot. Can you imagine a guy faking it? I came back to Boston to endure more torture. When I was leaving for LA, Raj and J were visiting family in India and were going to be there for a month. This meant, Mr. Bell was going to be all alone at home for the few days I was on the west coast. Of course it also meant I had to take care of the house for a month with absolutely no help. You see, Mr. Bell never helped around the house. We had turns to take out the trash or clean the bathroom and things like that. But Bell would never ever do it. As a matter of fact, some of his closest friends had refused to take him as a roommate because of his living habits. I came back to Boston from LA at night and saw that there were two full trash bags lying in the kitchen and as he was the only one home, I would have expected Bell to take them out. I knocked on his door and asked him to come out and look at the trash. He was on the phone but lazily came out while still talking on the phone. I told him that he should take the bags out otherwise I might have rat infestation. No sooner had I said that and lifted up the bags, two rats fled away from the security of their new home. Bell looked at me and signaled that he would take out the trash after he got off the phone. After a while, I went into his room and he was sound asleep and the bags were still there. From that day onwards, I decided to never depend on Bell for anything. He was on an internship too just like me and had to travel half the distance of what I had to, maybe even less. But this guy was so lazy that after I got out of the house in the morning to go to work, he would call me to ask how cold it was outside. All he had to do was open his laptop and check the weather but no he had to call me every single morning. Another thing that was part of his daily routine, or rather his nightly routine, was to watch porn every single night before he slept. As he shared the room with Raj, he could not do whatever he had to in the room. So he would watch porn and go to the bathroom. It was next to impossible for us to use the bathroom any time after 10:00pm because you never knew when his urge to go would come. All in all, Mr. Bell was definitely a role model when it came to ideal roommates. I really pity the poor woman who will marry him. Not only will she be doing all the work around the house, she will also be watching porn with her husband every night. Marital bliss.

Work at Radiant was becoming monotonous, and also a bit boring. However, the cool thing about the company was that they would let me work from home in case of snow or heavy rain or if I was not feeling too good. Not to mention that I took full advantage of this but I definitely put in a lot of effort in working from home. Watching 3-4 movies in one day, while you are supposed to be working, is no child's play. As I have mentioned earlier, the bus to New Hampshire used to drop me about 10 minutes from work. Unfortunately, it was mid-winter and there was a lot of snow on the sidewalks due to which I had to walk on the roads, as close to the sidewalks as possible with cars zipping past me at about 100mph. My brother did not help with this dilemma as he kept reminding me that cars lose control in winter on the road and tend to slide on the ice formed on the road. Greg always left early from work at around 4:00pm as he would come in early. But if he ever had to stay back late, he would always make sure he dropped me to the bus stop. If anyone took a glance at his car, they would advice me to walk to the bus stop than go in that antique.

Greg's car was a unique one. I forgot the make, but it had those cool automatic seatbelts which would strap on as soon as you sit inside and start the car. But that was the only cool thing about the car. How that car was still functioning I have no idea. It really looked like he had just picked something up from the junkyard and drove it to work. Of course, the interiors were even better considering he had converted his car into a makeshift trashcan. Nothing that smelled would be thrown in the car. However, it definitely had a lot of paper, packets of chips, etc. lying around. Finally one day his car broke down and the mechanic told Greg that he could not give him the sticker which said that the car was safe for the environment, or to be on the roads in general. If my memory serves me right, he was not even able to sell it for scrap.

Some days, Greg and I would get so bored that we would go to the tennis court outside our office and play a set or two. The first time we decided to play was when Greg started telling me about his tennis prowess and how he goes for coaching too. I have barely played tennis in my life but I can hold my own. And looking at Greg, you would know that he is better at computer games/videogames than actual physical sport. Him being good at sports would be like a Miss World contestant talking about something other than world peace or global warming. Just cannot see it happening. So we decided to play one day and he got his rackets. I decimated him 6-0. Poor guy was just devastated and wanted a rematch. Since that day we played almost 2-3 times a week till my internship got over and I think he has just taken a handful of games, not sets but games, off me.

My love life was again going sour. Soniya's insecurities were getting the better of her. Every time she would be pissed off at me for anything, she would tell me how stupid I was for going to Northeastern over better schools like University of Southern California. I knew that I had made a big mistake in my life by selecting a school for a girl and not thinking about its consequences on my career but the way Soniya would make me feel was just pathetic. This girl was one of the most vindictive women I had ever met. Again to make things right, I decided to make a trip to LA. This time we stayed in the Chinatown in LA. We barely did anything interesting there. We decided to go out one night and decided on a club called Elevate which was on the top floor of a skyscraper. While standing in the line to get in, we suddenly heard something shatter on the road. It was a glass thrown down from the club! Everyone in the line moved as close to the building as possible. Within minutes, another glass shattered on the road. All the people in front of us left right at that moment and we rushed in. The place was pretty dead, with most of the people being older. However, Soniya managed to get drunk and I actually ended up having a good time with her. We went back home and she decided to make a sex tape. I was not going to say no to one of those. However, I was a gentleman enough to let her keep the video. To be honest, I didn't even think it was that hot. One thing I definitely took notice of in this recent trip of Los Angeles was that Soniya was more into the physical aspect more than I was. This was a bit disturbing again for me as I considered myself to be a pretty horny guy. Of course, all the calls of 'Daddy' did not help her cause one bit.

After I got back, I found out about a football tournament which was to happen in Boston in April. I called all my friends from undergrad who were in New York to come play. I even called Rehan but he very clearly said no and hung up the phone. But within a few minutes he called back and told me that he was willing to come. Though it was strange behavior, I was actually happy and excited that he was coming to Boston. I had not met him in a while and I really wanted to meet him and talk to him. If not anything else, I just wanted to set things straight if possible. After I spoke to him, I started looking forward to April 2009.

Meanwhile, Soniya and I started have more chat sessions using the webcam. She had transferred to Berkeley, one of the really reputed schools in the US and was living alone which meant she could webcam almost every night. I had my own webcam to begin with but then after it stopped working, I used the Macs in the computer lab to chat. This girl was so into dirty talk and some sort of physical stuff that she would even do stuff on the webcam when I was actually sitting in the lab! By stuff I mean showing off body parts. I was extremely sure I would be banned from the computer lab for life like the bum who once managed to sneak in somehow and started watching porn on the computers. She would want to webcam with me almost every day. Once I had just come back after football and she wanted to chat. I was extremely tired but she did not want to hear any of that. Actually I was afraid to tell her no. Being the vindictive little brat she was, I did not know what she would do or how she would react. I was lying down on the bed chatting with her. Again she got into her ever horny mode, and started showing me our little video we had made in LA. After the video got over, she looked at her window only to see me sleeping. You have no idea for how long I had to take shit for that.

I was definitely taking a lot of crap from Soniya but with all the guilt of doing that to Rehan I really wanted to make it work. She once even got pissed off when I told her I am going to sleep early because I had to get up early to watch

Chelsea vs Manchester United the next day. She created a big scene about how watching a stupid football game was more important than talking to her. First of all, it was Chelsea vs Manchester United. Secondly, anyone who even knew me a bit would know how important football was to me. But this girl who was dating me did not understand that. My life was slowly turning into a living hell. I was just looking forward to April so that I could meet Rehan and let go off that guilt, and finally let go of the psychopath a.k.a. Soniya.

Anecdote : Tiger and his John

Recently, Tiger Woods and John Terry came into the limelight more than they had bargained for. Both were caught for extra marital affairs with numerous women, and had to pay dearly. Apart from their wives obviously being pissed off, Tiger lost out on a lot of endorsements, while Terry lost his captaincy for the national squad. Here is my take on this situation. While they had sex with every woman they saw, they were doing great in the careers! Tiger was the number 1 ranked golfer in the world, while Terry one of the best defenders on the planet. So they slept around a bit though they were married and have kids; big deal. A lot of sportsmen might be doing this. It is just that these two were unlucky enough to get caught. Considering their performances during their promiscuous times, I say let them sleep around. As a matter of fact, I would like to take it a step further and say make it a compulsion for every sportsman sleep around. Can you imagine the competition in such a world?

Devil wears floral patterns

April 2008 came really quick. I was excited the day all my friends were coming to Boston, but more importantly Rehan. I was also a bit afraid that he might stab or shoot me so I had asked all my friends to be on their toes when he arrived. For the couple of days they were all over, we were to live at a friend's house in Framingham. My friend Psycho was the first one to reach Boston and he picked me up on the way to Framingham. As we were in the car, I got a call from my team captain that the game was cancelled because of the heavy snow that day. Not only was it cancelled, the tournament was now postponed till June. Psycho and I were really dejected but at the same time we had to inform the others who had just left from New York. I made the call to Vamsi, and asked him where they were. He was really apologetic and told me that they were held up in traffic but now had just got out of NY City. At that moment I told him, "Oh ok, just come here fast."

So I didn't tell them the tournament was cancelled. But I didn't tell them it was still on either. I wanted to meet all of them really badly, and of course Rehan was the priority. And hanging out with these guys always made me forget whatever problems I had in my life. And man did I have problems. I was dating the devil. After a few hours, these guys reached our temporary abode. Surprisingly, things between Rehan and me were extremely normal. It was just like nothing had happened. We hugged, hung out, met Mary and had a lot of alcohol. I did get a few curses hurled at me for not informing about the tournament being cancelled, but in the end everyone was happy to meet up. The next day was Saturday and we all decided that we were definitely going to go out and party. I decided not to meet Mary for a change before going out but Rehan decided otherwise and drove us down to Boston. We were to pre-game at a bar before we hit the club. As we were all having drinks at the bar, guess who walks in through the door? Shilpa!

I was completely shocked to see this woman. We were not on talking terms so I didn't bother to greet her in anyway, and neither did she. I asked Rehan what in the world was happening and he informed me that Vamsi, my best friend in the world, had invited her so that they could meet up. If only I knew she was coming, I would have at least dressed up better. Not that I had any feelings for her or something but you would always want to look good in front of someone who dumped you to prove what they were missing out on. However, we left for a club soon and I was relieved that Shilpa chose not to join us. All of us had a great time dancing the night away. Once we were out, I could see that Rehan was completely hammered and was in no position to drive. I told him that the one guy who was not drinking could drive. But he was not ready to listen to anyone. He wanted to drive and that was it. I really thought he wanted to drive the car into a truck or something in such a way that he could kill only me. We let him drive and somehow he got us home safely. The next morning Rehan got up very drowsily and asked, "How did we get home?"

We decided to have lunch in Boston and then they would leave by evening. As we strolled down Newbury Street, there she was again; Shilpa. That very morning, Rehan had told me that Shilpa and Crassy had broken up. It didn't make any difference to me considering I was not even thinking about this woman anymore. However, I think Rehan was trying to see if I would still be interested so that he could bitch about it to Soniya one way or the other. We all sat down for lunch and everyone was talking except me and Shilpa with each other. As a result, I got the feeling that the others were feeling a bit uncomfortable. To ease out the tension a bit, and to ensure that everyone had a good time, I started talking to Shilpa. It was all small talk, but gradually we started talking a lot, making fun of each other; basically the works. It was kind of surprising I could talk to her so much. After lunch, we decided to grab a few drinks. We sat at a pub and started having drinks; all this at 4pm on a Sunday. After an hour or so, I got a call from Soniya. I told her what I was up to, and also told her that Shilpa was there. Coupled with the fact that it was those days of the month for her, this news really messed her up; not that she specifically needed anything big to get her ticked off. She started crying on the phone telling me how I could do this to her, and that she was sure now about me not being over Shilpa. At that moment I didn't know if I wanted to kill her more or if I wanted to kill myself.

After hanging up on the phone, I was really ticked off and needed more alcohol. However, it was almost time for the gang from New York to leave, apart from Psycho who decided to stay back and leave the next morning. We said our goodbyes and then were wondering what to do next. It was just Shilpa, Psycho, and me. We decided to skip to the adjacent bar and have a few more alcoholic beverages. As we were drinking, I started realizing that Shilpa was hitting on me. After being with a woman for around one and a half years, you understand what she is up to. That is the thing about all exes. Just when you are completely over them, they come back into your life to screw everything up. It is like a universal game played by these people. I was a bit surprised but decided to go with the flow. After we were all pretty drunk, Shilpa insisted that we all go back to her place and watch a movie. At first, I was a bit uncomfortable and told her I wanted to go home. But upon being insisted by Psycho and Shilpa, I caved. As Psycho was sitting online trying to figure out which stupid Bollywood movie to watch at her place, I headed into the kitchen to grab some water. Shilpa followed me there telling me she had some Indian sweets which I would love. I have a major sweet tooth. So much so that I am sure I won't have any teeth left by the time I am 40. She handed me the sweets and while I was gobbling them down, she stood really close to me. I told her that I loved the sweets to which she moved a step closer to me saying that she knew I would like them. We stood there for a minute with each of us being able to feel the other person's warm breath on their face. But I just took a step back and said, "Let's go see what movie Psycho picked out."

I quickly headed into the bedroom, and sat next to Psycho on the computer. No sooner had I done that, a chat window popped up and it was Mr. Palindrome! I could not believe that Shilpa was still talking to this guy. And what was Mr. Palindrome saying? He was trying to ask Shilpa what she was wearing. I was so shocked that when Shilpa entered the room I asked her what the hell was going on. With a very nervous smile she said, "Oh that is how he is." But why the hell was she talking to a guy who tortured the hell out of her in the first place? I had lost respect for this girl earlier because of her continuing to see a guy who had slapped her. Now I felt pity for this girl. Was she really that lonely that she had to talk to a guy who had harassed her so much that every day she would be worried 24/7 about her folks finding out about some photos? I decided to let it go and watch the movie that Psycho had picked out, Race.

Half way through the movie, I was already irritated with it considering I had already seen it and it was a bad movie. I had just agreed to watch it again as the others hadn't seen it. Shilpa said something regarding the movie which I thought was pretty funny. To reward her for her efforts, I gave her a high five. Usually when you high five someone, as I believe it, the hands hit each other and move away. However, in this case, Shilpa's hand grabbed on to mine and didn't let it go. For a second I pondered what to do. Should I really cheat on Soniya considering the consequences could be deadly? Or should I see where this little gesture would lead to? Then I thought to myself, "Well as long as you are dating the devil, might as well play with fire." I let Shilpa hold on to my hand for a bit and then gently kissed her hand. She looked at me and signaled for me to ask Psycho to go sleep. I told Psycho the same and he was more than happy to oblige considering the movie was just mind-numbing. After Psycho left, Shilpa and I started kissing. However, within a few minutes she pulls away and tells me, "Anish, I can't do this. You have a girlfriend. I have morals and values." Back the morality truck for a minute here. To begin with, you dump me to go out with a friend of mine. Then, you hit on me the whole day and pretty much urge me to do something. And finally when I am doing something, you remember your morals and values? Do you have any idea how frustrating that was for me? I was cheating on the deadliest woman alive and now I won't even get anything for it? I decided it was futile to tell this girl anything and just went to sleep in the other room.

Come summer and Soniya was to visit me in Boston. Though I didn't enjoy the relationship much, she actually had a great sense of humor. Also, Rehan was again not talking to me for some reason and so I was back on the guilt trip. I made out an entire itinerary for when she was to come. When she came, we did everything possible. It was her first time in Boston and I made sure she saw every inch of the historic town. I also realized that her wardrobe consisted of everything that had floral patterns, even formal dresses which just was such bad taste. Her last night in Boston, we decided to go out to a club along with a couple of other friends. We had a good time and all of us were pretty intoxicated by the end of the night. After we got home, Soniya started crying as to why we did not have much "alone" time at home. She blamed me for planning things in such a way that I did not have to spend any time alone with her. After arguing over this for a while, she asked me for a glass of water. At that point in my life, I only had one coffee mug. It was a gift given by my SNFT friends and I loved it because it had pictures of the SNFT clan. Unfortunately, it had a picture of Shilpa and me too. Soniya saw this picture and burst out crying. She cried and forced me to throw the mug away! Though it was of sentimental value, I had to throw it away to just shut this female dog up and go to sleep.

By the end of summer, my internship had ended and I had a month before my last semester at Northeastern University was to begin in August 2008. I decided to go to Colorado to visit my brother and his dogs and be there for around three weeks before I got back to the grind. It had been 2 years since I had come to the US and had still not gone back to India. Not only were there monetary issues, I thought I would go before I start working for a good month so that I get enough time to spend with all my friends, and family. Soniya was excited about me coming to Boulder, CO, and suggested that she could come there too as she had a month before school started as well. Though I just wanted to chill at my brother's house without any drama, I reluctantly agreed. Soniya arrived there a week after I reached. As she had a good sense of humor, my brother seemed to like her. However, even there she started throwing tantrums for small reasons. For example, one day I realized that Shilpa's sister was not on my Facebook any more for some reason. I was still very close to her so was a bit surprised that she had taken me of the networking website. I messaged her asking her why she took me off. This message really ticked off Soniya. She started complaining about how she was to believe I was over Shilpa if I did things like that. I just wanted to buy Soniya a gun so that she could just kill me instantly rather than torturing me to death slowly.

I returned to Boston to stay with new roommates. Third

apartment in Boston with third set of roommates. My close friends Patil and Bhatia again decided that they did not want me as their official roommate though I was always at their place 24/7. However, Patil did manage to find a bunch of guys who were looking for a new roommate. I reluctantly moved in with the new bunch. I had 5 roommates this time around. RKP was the supposed head of the house, or so he liked to believe. He was a year junior to me at NU, however, he talked as if he had been around for ages. Also, this guy was really desperate. Really would actually be an understatement considering he would hit on anything that moved just to get laid. My second roommate was Prasanna. Prasanna is the same guy who pronounced Chihuahua as Chi-hu-hu-ha-ha. However, he was a really cool guy, and very smart. I really respected him. Third was Sai. Though Sai was in London when I moved in, as soon as he returned we really hit it off. We both were very similar and we both had mutual respect for each other. The last two roommates were new to NU and were to start their first semester there. One was Amit Sharma who I liked because of two reasons. First of all, he was a cool guy and had a good sense of humor which I really respect in people. Secondly, he used to work out a lot in India before jaundice hit and he had to stop everything. So he was really helpful in telling me how to do exercises at the gym. I am not jacked and I doubt I ever will be. But I would like to stay fit. My final roommate was Venky. Where do I start with this guy?

Venky was definitely one of the dumbest, if not the dumbest, people I had ever met in my life. The others told me that it had a lot to do with him meeting Mary pretty often when he was in India. However, the dumbness of this guy was beyond any reasoning. Let me give you some examples. We were all talking about great minds of our generation one day and Steve Jobs came up. As soon as he heard about Jobs, he said, "Jobs? Where are the jobs? I want a job." Then, once he wanted to know how to get to New England from Boston. Considering that New England is made up of a few states in the Northeast like Massachusetts, Maine, Connecticut and a few others, and considering Boston is in Massachusetts, it would have been a bit difficult to give him the directions, but we managed to somehow. Venky always took classes which had at least a couple of our roommates in it so that he could just copy the assignments, and he himself never had to do them. He would sit at home all day and do nothing but smoke. If he went to school, he would play pool the whole day. Apparently, pool was the best game in the world*. His good run finally came to an end as he was caught for plagiarism. He was really tensed up as if he got an 'F', he would have to repeat the class and pay the fees again. After a nail biting week, the professor let him off the hook with a 'C'. He was relieved. However, unlike others who would have sworn off copying after such a traumatic week, he swore to never take classes from that department again because the chances of getting caught for plagiarism were higher.

The last semester with these guys was kind of fun. Sai, Prasanna, Amit and I would make a lot of fun of Venky and RKP as they were the supposed cool guys of the house.

*That is like saying Celina Jaitley is the best actress in Bollywood.

Academically, I had taken two really tough classes but was still doing well, somehow. Everything seemed great, apart from my relationship of course. For everyone else, Soniya was this hot girl. Whenever someone told me that, I became a bigger fan of Photoshop. I had seen this girl Photoshop our pictures as well, and the transformation was just too much. But considering I was seeing this woman at that point, I didn't mind people thinking she was hot. Soniya was living alone and wanted me to visit her at Berkeley. Though I should have ended things a long time back, I just couldn't every time I thought about what I did to Rehan. So soon enough I was on my way to Berkeley. I reached her place and she was more than excited to see me. She immediately started engaging in unmentionables. But I think I had reached the threshold of tolerating this woman. I just could not perform any more. This was the first time this had ever happened to me. This was the first time I realized how important a mental connection is with someone if you want to have a physical relationship. Of course, Soniya started crying because she thought it was because I thought she was fat. As if I was not annoyed enough earlier, her crying was really pissing me off. I tried to tell her it was nothing like that, and we tried it a few times the following days as well but to no avail. And every time we tried and failed, I had to listen to her crying for hours. After four days, I was just glad to get out of that hell hole.

Upon returning to Boston, Soniya and I spoke a lot on the phone with her making efforts to reconcile the relationship. However, in a few days, she called me and told that it was over. The minute she said that, I wanted to scream, "YES!" But instead I asked her why and told her we could work things out. But she was adamant about it, and reiterated the fact that things were not going great and that it would be better for us to end things. After a couple of not so great attempts to deter her from this decision, I said ok. But as soon as I said ok, she started crying about how I was running behind Shilpa to get back with her and that now I was not showing any interest of any sort when it came to her. Just when I thought all the torture was over, this girl was screwing with my head even after she had broken off things with me.

I had planned my graduation carefully. I wanted to get some experience under my belt before I graduated so that it would help me finding a full time job for which I worked for 6 months at Radiant. One thing that I did not anticipate however was the great economic crisis which was about to hit the country. This was a bigger hit on the economy than The Great Depression. All students who were about to graduate in December 2008 were tensed. With unemployment on the rise, how could foreign nationals get jobs? How would new graduates with barely any experience get jobs when there were so many experienced people sitting in the market jobless? These were definitely tough times and I was really scared about the future. I started applying for jobs in October itself but with little or no results. By the time I graduated, I had no job and a lot of loans. How was I going to deal with this? Would I be able to find a job any time in the future and repay my loans? These questions kept haunting me.

Though we had broken up, Soniya and I kept in touch. I really didn't want to and would always be looking for a reason to stop talking to her. Close to new years, she told me that she was going to visit Rita in New Jersey, and that I should come stay there for a couple of days. I was against the idea, however, it also meant meeting up with a couple of other friends, namely Psycho and Vamsi who were going to be in New York for new years. I went to New Jersey and as I was waiting for Rita to buzz me into the building, Soniya opens the door and hugs me, and goes on to kiss me. I had no clue that we were friends with benefits but apparently that was the case. I pulled away as quickly as I could and we made our way upstairs. Once I had settled down, I realized that Rita and Soniya were up to the same thing they were last December, bitch about everyone in their high school. These people really needed a life.

I was really getting frustrated with them as that was all they did day in and day out. I wanted a break and soon called Vamsi asking him what he was doing for new years. Soniya and Rita decided not to do anything for the auspicious day as it was extremely cold outside, which was cool with me. But I did not want to sit at home another minute and listen to them talk about their schoolmates. Vamsi told me he was going for a house party. I asked him if I could crash it but he was very skeptical about it so I dropped that plan. We decided to meet up the following night for a couple of drinks. The next night Psycho, Vamsi, another friend from undergrad Shetty and me met up at a bar. We were having an awesome time when Soniya started calling. It was about 1am in the night and she was telling me how I should come home early because it was not good etiquette to come home late to a person's house where you were a guest. She was completely right about that so I told her that I would just hang out with my friends till this place closed and then would stay over at Psycho's, and come home in the morning so that no one will have to get up late in the night. This did not sit well with her. She again started crying and created a lot of drama. I finally grew a pair and told her I was going over to Psycho's and that was it. I hung up the phone and switched it off so that she would not annoy the hell out of me anymore.

After we got out of the bar at around 3am, we went to this diner to grab something to eat. As we sat down on the table, we saw a couple of $20 on the table. As we were all drunk, someone whispered to pick it up. Being all courageous at that time after telling off the she-devil, I took one bill and put it in the pocket. When the waitress came to collect the previous bill, she noticed that there was $20 less on the table. We told her that that was the only bill on the table but she was going to take none of that. She called the manager and after a long discussion, we told him to just add the extra $20 to our bill so that it would be taken care off. However, our little stunt did not sit well with the waiters and no one was ready to serve us. We got frustrated after waiting for 15 minutes and got up to leave. Psycho and I went over to the manager and gave him the $20 we had picked up saying that we found it under the table and left. But just as we were leaving, the waitress who was really ticked off with us told us to wait as she was calling the cops. I was sweating like a dog in a Chinese restaurant at this point.

As we were waiting outside trying to tell the waitress the story of the note that had fallen under the table, a drunken passerby heard our conversation and decided to help us. Psycho and Vamsi went ahead to see if we could get anything to eat while Shetty and I waited for the cops. The passerby told the waitress that he would talk to the manager and take care of it. While she was still on the phone, we went in and this new friend of ours tried to convince the manager as to how he knew us well and how we could never do anything like steal money. The manager was really frustrated and just asked us to leave. We came out to find two cops waiting for us. Shetty and I tried to explain to the cops what the situation was. While we were doing that, our new friend tried to intervene. The cops asked him if he was involved too, and told him that if we were found guilty and if he was involved, he would be locked up too. And just as fast as we had made a new friend, we lost him too. He ran faster than I had seen any man run. We again started convincing the cops that the $20 bill had just fallen below the table. They were not buying our story but they got a call on their radios saying that there was a fight in the bar down the street. The cops started leaving when we asked them what we should do. One of them just said, "Get the hell out of here."

We ate something and headed out. I slept over at Psycho's and got up early to get back to Rita's. When I reached her place, there was a lot of silence. Apparently, Soniya thought that I had offended Rita by staying out all night. How the hell had I offended her? Coming back home late in the night would have meant troubling her for no rhyme or reason. Doesn't just coming home early in the morning make more sense? I didn't want to leave from the place early because I was meeting these guys after a long time and wanted to spend time with them. But all my justifications fell on deaf ears. Soniya wanted me to grab my things and leave. She was throwing me out of the house! I called Psycho to come pick me up and went over to his place before leaving for Boston the next day. I decided never to talk to the psychotic woman again. To this day, she still wonders why we cannot be friends.

I stayed in Boston for a whole month looking for jobs but to no avail. The job market was really down and I could not find anything. My brother suggested that I come over to Boulder and stay with him as that would at least mean not having to pay or rent or food. It made a lot of sense and by February 2009, I was in Boulder. In a last gasp effort to find a job, I joined one of those fake Indian consultants, the ones about whom I have mentioned before, the same guys who train you in something and then fake your resume. After Business Analyst training for a good 2 months, they informed me that they did not have job openings either.

There went $1000 I was never going to see again. Simultaneously, I was looking for jobs independently as well but it was of no use.

I always wanted to go for higher studies even after my masters. PhD was always something on my mind and as the job scene was bad, I decided to apply for PhD. Unfortunately, I could only apply to Northeastern as I had some problems in obtaining my undergraduate transcripts. I got great letter of recommendations from Radiant and from a professor at NU itself. This definitely helped as soon enough I found out that I had gotten admission into PhD and would be starting in August. Can you imagine a guy like me doing PhD? Actually, can you imagine if I were to go on and become a professor? I think I already feel bad for the kids of the next generation.

Apart from the fruitless task of looking for jobs in spite of getting a PhD admission, I had a good time living with my brother. I would sit at home and play with the dogs all day, or play FIFA 2009 on his Xbox 360, or cook. I had never cooked in the 2 and half years I was in the US. But now that I had enough free time, I would cook a lot of things looking at recipes. I got so much into it that I even used to watch the Food network channel almost all day, and even knew which show was at what time! I absolutely love cooking now and I think it is something every guy should learn and love to do. Women have to endure a lot of things in their lifetime like the monthly problems, pregnancy etc. The least we could do is cook for our better halves.

My brother and I would also have a drink every night before dinner. Friday nights were barbeque nights which meant a lot of drinking and eating some nice grilled meat. We barely ever stepped out of the house apart from going to the theatre to watch movies. I started getting bored of sitting at home all day and started playing badminton and football. I played in the Men's A league indoors and Co-ed B div team outdoors. The name of my co-ed team was Shag Nasty. Badminton was fun too. I played my first badminton tournament in the division B and easily won it. In the next win I decided to take it to the next level and played division A where I was made to look like a fool by a man who was well in his late forties or early fifties. Soon I made a lot of friends through football and badminton. A couple of days before my birthday, my badminton friends decided to go out. As my birthday was on Monday, it was decided that we would celebrate it Saturday night itself.

As Boulder barely had any clubs, we drove to Denver as there were a lot of options there. We ended up at a place which had Bollywood nights. The DJ was a friend of my brother's so I was happy to go there. We had quite a bit to drink and I was enjoying some attention from some ladies as well. However, I did not want to talk to anyone as I was just not in the mood for anything after being tortured to death by the last girl I was with. After a while, I was tired and decided to sit down for a bit. Knowingly or unknowingly, I decided to sit next to two girls. To be honest, I did not even notice them as such till I sat down. They were pretty decent looking girls, and the one sitting farther away from me was really cute. The girl sitting next to me started talking to me and started asking me why I was not dancing. I asked her the same question in a bid to start conversation somehow so that she would introduce me to her cute friend. It did work and I was introduced to her. Her name was Heena.

Anecdote : How to not act - By Bollywood actresses

Bollywood has a lot of actresses. Lot is actually an understatement. Every year the Miss India winner gets into Bollywood, along with a lot of daughters of yesteryear actors/actresses. The main criterion for getting into Bollywood is looking good, and not talent. Don't get me wrong, there are some great actresses like Shabana Azmi who are just amazing. But then the rest of them are just in movies as eye candy. I don't have a problem with eye candy, just like the millions of other male viewers. However, it gets annoying when these so-called actresses start addressing to their "fans". How can you call a bunch of people who look at you dancing in the rain and touch themselves fans? Are there really people who admire these women for their acting skills? I recently came across a big fan of one of the top actress in Bollywood today. This woman charges crores of rupees to do a single film. I asked this guy to name one movie where the actress had done a good job and all he could say was she looked so good in so and so movie. The high point of these actresses addressing to their fans was when Riya Sen said something like, "I am sorry to disappoint my fans." My dear Riya, I highly doubt you got many "fans". And even if you do, they are mostly people who want you to not say a single word and just go on a vacation with them.

Home coming

Heena was really interesting. In the club itself, I was really into this girl. You all know my take on meeting girls at clubs. But here I was thinking about anything but a physical relationship with this woman. Also, she was from Delhi! My views on Delhiites were definitely prejudiced based on my experiences with Doggy and J. However, I forgot all this and started talking to this girl. She had just finished her masters in architecture from Columbia University, one of the best schools in the country. To try to impress her a bit, I said the few lines in Punjabi I have learned from my dear GHK high school, and it definitely seemed to work. We had a great conversation but she left wishing me a happy birthday in advance without giving me her number, and without asking for mine. I was a bit disappointed to see her go but at the same time I was so into this woman that I was determined to find her.

The whole of next day I spent in trying to find Heena on Facebook and Orkut but to no avail. There were absolutely no traces of this mystery woman. I gave up. But the DJ at the club the previous night came to my rescue. Someone had taken a video of that night and so he tagged people whom he knew had come there. I was one of them, and one was Hinna.

No wonder I could not find this girl. I had gotten the spelling all messed up. However, though I had a feeling it was the same person, there was no way of confirming it as her Facebook profile was more secure than Fort Knox. I decided to send out a casual message asking her if she was the same person I had met the previous night. I waited anxiously for the reply, and it finally came after two days confirming that she was in fact the same girl. We started messaging each other on Facebook every day. I could not meet her as she was on a road trip of the US with her friends. I found out that she loved travelling and that she had been to more countries than I had been to places within India itself. She had also planned a Euro trip the following month with the same friends. The part that I most respected about this girl was that she was doing it all with her own hard earned money. I know a lot of people who have travelled around the world, but those trips would be sponsored by their parents. This girl was responsible enough to go the other way and I absolutely respected that. She also told me that she was recently out of a relationship of over 5 years. They were even supposed to get married but the guy was a complete loser. He had kept naked pictures of his ex on his computer, and when Hinna caught him with them, he refused to delete them. Though she somehow let that go*, the guy had installed keylogger on her laptop so he could find out her passwords. I could not believe such guys exist in these times. First of all you keep indecent pictures of your ex, and then you don't trust your understanding girlfriend?

I could relate to the tumultuous relationship she had just endured considering I had just gotten out of a similar one with Soniya. I shared my past relationships with her too and she was more than understanding. We both decided that we did not want to be in a relationship but at the same time we definitely wanted to meet each other after she was back from her little road trip. According to Cosmopolitan magazine, when a guy says, "I would like to see you but I don't want to

*Talk about understanding girlfriends.

be in a relationship, he usually means I want to screw you." I do admit I had somewhat of those sentiments, but at the same time I was also very much into this girl. After a week she finally got back from her road trip and I was excited to meet her. Unfortunately, I did not have her phone number and she had mine as I was stupid enough to put it up on my profile on Facebook. The smart woman that she was, she would call me every day but only after she made sure she blocked her number. One fine Thursday morning I get a call from her saying, "I am right outside your house. I am going to give you 5 minutes to lock up the dogs."

I was sitting at home looking like a bum. Now that she was right outside, I did not even have time to change or even do something to at least make me look presentable. The last time Hinna saw me, it was dark and I can look good in the dark. But looking at me in daylight is a whole new ballgame, and now I did not even have time to look presentable somehow. I quickly locked up the dogs and opened the door. She came out of the car wearing a simple white top and blue jeans. I have mentioned many-a-times how I am totally into tall, dusky and petite women. Hinna was the exact opposite of that description. She was short, fair, and quite petite. Actually I was glad she was not a size zero* girl, like many these days. But I was so smitten by this girl after talking to her just a few times, I really was ready to let go of all my must-haves in a girl. We sat at my place for around 4 hours and just spoke. I had a

*You know whom I blame for women dying for size zeros? Popeye and Bluto! If these nitwits had gone for the more voluptuous women around rather than Olive, women would have been healthier today.

girl alone at home, and not once did I think of making a move. All I wanted to do was talk and it was great too. We spoke about things from our childhood to pretty much everything. Around 5pm, she got up to leave.

Before I opened the door, I held her hand and pulled her towards me. We kissed and it was the best kiss of my life. There were instant sparks; more than when I was electrocuted as a kid. I wanted to see more of this girl.

Our next meeting was for some stupid Bollywood movie. I hated Hindi movies, but I was ready to drive 45 minutes to the theatre so that I could spend some time with Hinna. She was supposed to go on her Euro trip in a couple of days so after the movie, we went to grab her favorite beverage at Barista, Green Tea Frappachino, and talk for a while. She kept asking me to meet her in New York as she was to stay there for a week or so after she got back from her trip. This was another thing about Hinna. She absolutely loved New York. So much so that someone like me, who loathed that city, loved hearing about it from her. I would just keep imagining us together on the streets on New York. What was happening to me? I did not even know this girl and I was already day dreaming. I would have loved to meet her in New York and spend a whole week with her. However, I was not in the best financial state to make a trip like that. Hinna even agreed to pay for my tickets and take care of the stay. I was a bit uncomfortable with her doing that. I am no male chauvinist who has a problem with a woman paying or anything of that sort. It was just that it would have been our first trip together and I should at least have been able to hold my own. I graciously declined the offer, and told her I could not wait to meet her after a month.

While Hinna was away, I kept myself busy with football. But every other day, I would get an email from her saying what she was up to in Europe. It was sweeter considering that she barely had any internet access there, but the first thing that she would do was email me. She even sent me postcards from four cities, including New York before she left for the trip. The biggest surprise was this huge card I got from the Allianz Arena. I had just casually mentioned to her that when she was in Munich, she should try and visit the Allianz Arena as it was one of the most beautiful football stadiums in the world, and as an architect she would love it too. Just because I had said that, she had gone there and got me a postcard. No one had ever done something so nice for me. I cannot express how good I felt every time I got a card from her. I could not wait for her to get back.

Life is funny. It always gives you these highs but at the same time, soon enough, you get the lows too. And mine was just around the corner. My mom was admitted in the hospital with some infection. Though it seemed minor, it was later diagnosed to be Non-Hodgkin's Lymphoma; blood cancer.

My brother immediately booked tickets and left for India within a month. I could not accompany him as I was on my OPT period which meant that if I were to go to India, I would not be allowed back in the country without a job offer. The land of opportunities was keeping me away from rushing home in such a situation. I was helpless but I was at least happy that my brother was going to be there for a while. To add to misery, I sprained my ankle during football the very next day my brother left. This meant taking two big German Shepherds for walks for 2 entire weeks. Of course my brother did extend his trip to 3 weeks but I did not mind. I was happy he did so that he could be around for any help if needed. Hinna came back to Denver a couple of days before my brother were to come. We both decided it was best for her to rest for a couple of days as she was just back from a long journey. The day I was to pick up my brother, I left early and went to Hinna's house which was about 10 minutes away from the airport. She had gotten a lot of chocolates of which she gave me some. But the best part was she got me a Czech Republic football t-shirt! I had mentioned to her once how I loved the national team and she remembered that to get me a t-shirt when she was there. Was the woman perfect or what? Not only was she considerate, I could do anything with her without getting bored or annoyed. I am a very picky person but she just changed everything about me. Another thing I noticed was Hinna was from a very well-off family. In spite of this, she always made sure wherever she went, or whatever she did, almost all of what she would spend would be her own hard-earned money and not her parents'. She told me she had worked on campus during her undergraduate years at CU Boulder as a DJ, a security guard etc. and saved as much as possible so that she could go on trips like the one in Europe. You have no idea how much this impressed me. I knew girls from middle-class families who would have high expectations and would want their parents to get everything for them. On the other hand, there was this girl who was definitely not from a middle-class family, but worked hard for whatever she wanted to do. My respect for this girl just went through the roof. This girl was more perfect than I could have imagined any girl I wanted in my life.

My brother came back with good news. He said that mom was recovering well after her chemotherapy. He also got back 3 bottles of Old Monk, the best dark rum ever. We did manage to finish them over a course of 3 weekends, but hey it was Old Monk.

I was acting like a 16 year old when it came to Hinna. Every time I saw her online, or saw her name on the caller id on the phone, I would have a huge grin on my face. Of course, I never ever told her that. I would always pretend to be this macho guy who was still in a place where he did not want to be in a relationship. But truth be told I was falling in love with this woman. Yes I said the 'L' word. And it was a scary thought. I barely knew this girl but I had such strong feelings for her. How could I not fall in love with this girl? Strictly based on looks, she was extremely cute. And other than looks, she was the most amazing person I had ever met. She had her own opinion about everything, but would never force it upon anyone. At 25, she was the strongest, most independent woman I had ever met. I kept telling myself that I should not express these feelings I had for her. How would a girl who barely knew me for a few months react if I told her I felt so strongly about her? Hinna was more than open about her feelings, and always told me that she liked me. I still didn't have the courage to tell her how I felt.

After a couple of months of meeting each other

regularly, and going for a couple of Bollywood movies, anyone would have thought we were at least dating, if not in a relationship. However, I still hadn't had the courage to ask her to go out with me. I had even met her mom during one of the movies. On her birthday, we went out for sushi. I never would have gone for raw fish if she hadn't encouraged me to. We sat there at this small restaurant, having sushi and sake. I don't know if it was all the Bollywood movies she was making me watch, but life suddenly seemed like a Bollywood movie. The person you love sitting right opposite you in this dimly light, small place, looking gorgeous in a dress. Unfortunately, she was leaving for India in a few days. Did I mention I was going a day after that to India too? Yes, I was finally going back home after 3 and half years. I was to stay in India till Jan 20th and then go to NU to start my PhD studies. You have no idea how excited I was the minute I booked my tickets.

Hinna left on Dec 1st, making sure that we would meet up in India. She was to come to Mumbai for her friend's wedding; the same friend who had introduced us at the club. I was very happy that she was coming to Mumbai. I wanted to take her around the city, and couldn't wait for her to meet my friends. I packed my bags and soon enough found myself waiting at the airport. I had a couple of connecting flights. I was to fly from Denver to Washington DC, Washington DC to Dubai, and Dubai to Mumbai. The flight to DC was pretty uneventful. However, the next flight to Dubai was something. Every American Airlines flight apparently has a US Marshal in plain clothes to ensure safety of the flight in case of a hijacking situation. And in our flight, this guy was sitting right next to me! Of course, it's not like he told me he was a marshal but you didn't have to be Einstein to figure it out. To begin with, this guy had a crew cut. Secondly, each airhostess came to him every 10-15 minutes to whisper a seat number to him of people they thought were suspicious. If these people want to keep this operation under the radar, they really ought to hire some smart air-hostesses. The most disappointing part about the 13-hour flight from Washington DC to Dubai was that they did not serve any alcoholic beverages. I think even economy class fliers are entitled to free alcohol considering it is a 13-hour flight. How in the world do you expect anyone to sleep? As a result, I could barely get any shut-eye. We reached Dubai airport and I was just shocked to see it. It was a monstrosity. I walked for half-an-hour to get to my connecting flight. Soon enough, we took off from Dubai. For the first time in my years of flying via planes, I found the airhostess attractive. And they were serving alcohol too on his 2-hour flight! Booze served by good-looking women is never a good combination. I was not really looking much considering I was only thinking about one woman at this point in my life. However, the old Gujarati guy sitting in front of me seemed to be enjoying himself. He got drunk after two miniatures of scotch and was flirting with the extremely attractive South African air-hostess. I was recently told that flirting is good for health even if you are in a relationship, and I agree. But flirting by being loud and obnoxious, and interfering in other people's conversations with the same woman is never good. Actually, that is harmful to your health considering you could get beat up pretty easily. In the end, I was just happy it was only a 2-hour flight and we landed in *aamchi Mumbai* soon.

The flight was on time so my SNFT group who were to pick me up wouldn't have to wait much, or at least I thought so when I landed. I kept waiting for my luggage to come. However, after waiting for about an hour, I only got 1 bag out of the 2 I had checked in. What a great welcome back to the country. This also meant I had to go report missing baggage which took another hour. By the time I was out, it was 4:30 am and I had asked my friends to pick me up at 2:30am. I frantically searched for a public phone. By the time I called them it was almost 5am, and I was worried if they might have gone back home. Luckily, they were driving around the airport. Within no time, they picked me up. It was great to see all my childhood friends after so long. As it was almost daybreak, we decided to part ways after they dropped me home. We did make plans to spend the whole of Saturday at Sahil's new house in Kalamboli, a place that I had heard of for the first time in my life in spite of being in Mumbai for 23 years, as it was his birthday on Saturday. I called home and told my folks I was on my way. It was a tough job to carry my checked in bag and carry on to the third floor via stairs. At that point, I was actually happy one bag had gone missing. My dad had kept the door open for me. As I walked in I saw my mom sitting on the couch, waiting for me. When I left in 2006, my mom was in the pink of her health with beautiful long black hair and a smile that would just capture anyone's heart. In contrast to that image, in front of me sat a woman who was extremely weak, had no hair, and had no reason to smile. As soon as she saw me, she stood up and came to me, hugged me and started crying. My heart dropped.

One thing that waited for me at home was my biggest enemy; the Indian toilet. Though I had been used to it for almost my whole life, 3 years of relaxing on a western toilet had made me lazy. I did not want to take that much effort to relieve myself. I actually realize now that it is a very good workout. Anyway, in a few hours time, I had told my folks about the journey back home and filled them in on the details of the missing baggage. It was almost 9am and I really wanted to sleep considering I barely managed to get any in the plane. But I had one person to call before I could sleep; I had to call Hinna. She was in Chandigarh with her family at that time and I had the number that she was to use. I called her and was extremely happy to hear her voice after just 48 hours or so. This girl was definitely one silver lining in my life. I spoke to her for a bit before hitting the sack. The next thing I knew was opening my eyes in the evening only.

I had already made plans to go play football in the evening in my old colony, Reserve Bank of India quarters. Playing there was more nostalgic than I could have ever imagined it would be. I came back home tired and quickly hit the sack thinking of the long day that was to be Saturday. By noon, my friend Mathew picked me up to go to Kalamboli. While he was driving, I realized there was some constant noise coming from his car, and the other cars on the road. At first, I did not recognize it. Then I figured it out; it was honking. For 3 years, I don't remember listening to any cars honk unless I was in New York*. For everything, the drivers would press the horn as much as possible. Be it immovable traffic jams, which

*Hinna even made the sounds of cars in New York sound amazing.

cannot be solved in anyway by honking, to pedestrians just walking on the side of the road, the cars did their mandatory noise. One thing that they did not honk to was cows. There was a cow standing in the middle of the road, eating grass that was growing on the divider. Each car slowly and quietly maneuvered their way past the cow. If only they thought of other cars as cows, the noise pollution in the city would have been under control.

Another thing that really caught my eye in Mumbai were the hoardings for the clothing store Seasons. The model featuring on these ads was apparently Miss Mumbai 2009, and there was a big debate if her name was Roshan Khambatta or Neha Dalvi. Whatever your name is miss, you are the most beautiful woman I have ever seen in the entire life. So much so, that I wanted to wear those clothes by Seasons, even though they are strictly for women only! It took us 3 full hours to reach Sahil's house through the traffic. Once there, Sahil had already bought beers which were perfect considering the heat and humidity. I had also got a bottle of 18yr old Glen Fiddich from the duty free shop at the Mumbai airport so that we could celebrate Sahil's birthday in style. Mathew and I were the first ones to reach there. The rest of the gang started pouring in one at a time and we were soon on our way to drunken bliss. I had told my friends that I could now cook and I decided to cook even after having a few drinks and made a vegetarian dish which was edible. However, the chicken dish was pretty bad. Actually, it was so bad that the stray dogs in the complex weren't ready to eat it. As a result, all of us had to starve and drink ourselves to sleep. But no matter what, hanging out with all of them after this huge gap felt good. We all slept pretty late in the night only to wake up early as Sahil's family was to come join us in the morning.

All of us were pretty hungry and decided to eat at McDonalds. I know the chain started in the US, but the food at Indian McDonalds is way better than its counterpart in the US. After lunch, we decided to make a trip to Lonavala with Sahil's family. It was a great trip and all in all, we enjoyed our reunion. I reached back home Sunday night and immediately hit the sack.

The next few days were a blur to me. I would sleep all day, and only get up to eat. Whenever I did get up, I spoke to Hinna. I could not wait for her to come to Mumbai. She was to reach here on the 25th of Dec. Unfortunately, I had a little trip of my own to make before that and would only be back on the 26th. My trip was to my native town in Kerala.

I was not sure if my mom should have been travelling considering she was quite weak. But my grandmother and aunts really wanted to see her, and me, as they had not seen me in a while, and had not seen my mom since they found out about her not being well. We took the flight to Cochin from where a car was to pick us up. My uncle who had married into the family was there with one of my cousins. I had not seen my cousin in my years and he had had a major growth sprout in that time. This kid was only in the 8th grade but was almost as tall as me. His father on the other hand had a different issue all together. As we all sat down for lunch, I noticed that my uncle's hand kept shaking while he tried to eat. Later on my mother told me that it was because he was a complete alcoholic, and had not had his daily dose that day which resulted in the shivering. This really gave me the creeps as I used to drink at every given opportunity. I just comforted myself by saying I am not as bad as that guy.

The drive back to our home was a long 5 hour journey. By the time we reached home, my rear was completely numb. But more importantly, it had taken a toll on my mom. She was really feeling weak and just wanted to lie down. As we live in quite a remote area, the neighbors came to greet us too. My elder aunt who was living with my grandmother helped my mom into the house but burst out crying seeing my mother's condition. While all this was happening, the neighbor started crying out loud. I was amazed that this elderly woman cared so much about my mother. However, she was crying about the loss of her husband about 7-8 months back. I understand your grievance but how can you not be considerate about our situation here? Does it really look like we were in any state to provide emotional support to anyone? This woman was the centre of attraction the whole night! How I missed my village.

The next couple of days were just spent in sleeping and watching TV. I kept calling Hinna to talk to her whenever possible. She told me about hanging out with some of her old friends, especially Ankit, an old friend who annoyed her every time they met by telling her how much he liked her and that they should get married. I really wish I was in Delhi with Hinna so that I could mark my territory and tell this guy to buzz off. This Punjaban was all mine and I was not going to give her up to anyone. However, I trusted her to deal with the situation. My third day there I met up with my cousin

Abhilash whom I hadn't met in over 5 years, and in that time he had gotten married too in spite of being jobless. It was great catching up with him considering we were really close when we were kids. And to commemorate this reunion, we decided to drink. And I thought my uncle was a pathetic loser.

Since that day, I started meeting friends around my house. All of them were elder to me but we all used to play together as kids so we were definitely excited to meet up. I realized that in the 5 years that I had not come back to Kerala, a lot had changed. All these guys were drunkards now. I seemed like a minion compared to them. They would finish one bottle of Brandy every day. And their method of having a drink was gulping it down. They did not believe in enjoying the drink at all. For the first few days, I stayed away from liquor considering I was already scared of becoming like my uncle. But then I joined them thinking it was my vacation any way so what the hell.

One day after having a few drinks, I called Hinna to talk to her. We had a good conversation as usual. She asked me for when she was to book her return tickets back to Delhi. I really wanted to tell her to just stay in Mumbai till I left on the 20th for Boston. I would have loved to spend that much time with her. But at the same time, that would have been selfish on my part. How could I keep her away for that long from her family and friends? Against my will, I told her to book her tickets back for 30th Dec itself so that she could spend the new years with her friends and then spend time with her family. After confirming the dates, I also told her that I would like to take this to the next level and would officially like to be dating her. I wish I could have told her how I really felt, but even after being tipsy I decided to keep my true feelings for her to myself and not scare her away. But then again, I had taken a big step in my book to finally be dating Hinna. I was happy that this was slowly but surely going somewhere; somewhere significant.

The next day I woke up happy. Happy that I was with the woman I wanted to be. Maybe not in a relationship, but I was so close to it. However, the happiness didn't last long as we had to rush my mom to the hospital because of this pain she was getting in her arm every night. She had to be admitted and stayed there for a few days. My friends would drive me to town whenever I wanted to go to the hospital, and then go pick up a bottle of brandy to drink. I wouldn't join them much but a couple of times I succumbed to temptation. And you might wonder what their source of entertainment was after getting drunk? Well it was to make me talk in an American accent because they didn't understand a word of it. Actually, they would barely understand a word of it even if I was speaking normally. The good thing about drinking with these guys was that they would always get me my favorite food in the world; Kerala parathas. If anyone has not had these ever in their life, you are missing out on something good. You know how the cocktail is named Sex on the Beach? Well considering how tasty these parathas are, they should be named Sex on a Plate.

After my mom was discharged, we were all a bit more relaxed back home. My father would try his level best to feed me everything possible, just like my aunts. They were surprised I had lost so much weight and that I was now as thin as a stick*. Every time I would refuse something, my dad would tell me, "But you used to eat/drink that when you were a kid." I heard so much of this statement that I got frustrated and the next time he said that, I told him, "Dad, I used to shit in my pants when I was a kid. Do you want me to do it now too?"

The day to go back to Mumbai was coming closer. Every day I would sit and wonder what all I would do with Hinna in Mumbai. Though I was born and raised there, I really had no idea where tourists would go in that city. I had to plan this well because I wanted this trip to be the best she had ever had though she had been all around the world. We spoke about what we would do in the 3 days I had her all to myself. Though she seemed excited, she also sounded a bit aloof. I asked her what the problem was. She said that she had to confess something. She told me that before we had started dating, she had kissed Ankit.

*I am actually fitter than I have ever been. I only need to gain around 30 kilos to be fit in their mind.

Anecdote : Black or White

Since I got back to India, I started seeing all the ads for fairness creams. There is even a Facebook application that makes your picture fairer! Big Bollywood stars endorse these products by saying things like, "What if you are not me? You can still be handsome by applying this fairness cream." What is wrong with us? Are we so obsessed with fair skin? I know I have tread upon this topic briefly earlier but seeing all these ads again really gets to me. It gives people the wrong idea that dark skinned people are not beautiful. As a result of these ads, all the fair skinned men in India think they look good. Each and every one of them! People, who are watching these ads and thinking I need to be fairer, please stop killing yourselves with these thoughts. You are all beautiful just the way you are. Skin color does not determine anyone's beauty. I am actually outraged at actors who endorse these products. All these actors take a stand against a lot of things like child labor, cruelty against women etc. How about taking a stand against discrimination based on color in India?

The Final frontier

My jaw dropped when Hinna said that. I have sprained my ankle a million times, been beat up by 15-20 guys, and have had Hernia, but this really hurt. I was really disappointed because this was a guy whom she didn't like and kept complaining about to me. I expressed my disappointment to her. But did I really have a reason to be disappointed? After all, I had never committed to her and always kept the nature of the relationship vague. Doesn't that give her every right to look for other suitors? Though I was not justified in being upset, the sweetheart that she was, she talked to me on the phone for a couple of hours till I felt better. And I actually did feel better by the end of our conversation. Wasn't this not incentive enough for me to tell her how I really felt about her?

The next morning I thought about it a lot and again my fear got the better of me. I decided to not say anything to her and just keep things the way they were. In a couple of days we left for Mumbai. I reached there on the afternoon of the 26th of Dec. The same evening was the reception that I was supposed to attend with Hinna. Trying to look as good as possible, I headed out towards the venue. I was going to meet some of her closest friends, and I just had to make a good impression. I reached there a bit early, and had to wait for Hinna and her couple of friends to get dressed and come down. Have you ever gone to a wedding where you don't know anyone but maybe a couple of people? It is a very awkward situation. For me, this was a test to prove I was good enough for this Delhi girl, and there was no way in hell I was going to back out of this one.

Soon enough, I saw Hinna walking coming towards me with her two friends, Shweta and Anita. Hinna was looking gorgeous in a green sari, with a shining silver border. She was definitely making some heads turn, and my eyes were stuck to her. I was introduced to her friends, and so the test began. The reception itself was grandiose. With 4-5 different styles of cuisines, and an open bar, I couldn't decide what to do first; eat or drink? The girls decided to have a couple of drinks so I joined them. I stuck to cocktails as I wanted to be completely in my senses, and not make a mess of anything. Every now and then, Hinna would tactfully excuse herself so that I would be alone with her friends. Though at first I was quite uncomfortable, I slowly started warming up to them and making more conversations. By the end of the night, I thought I had held the fort well. Late in the night I got a message from Hinna which said: Approved ☺ .

The whole of next day, Hinna was to spend with Shweta and they were to roam around Mumbai. This dampened my plans a bit as I was anyway falling short of places to take her to. They had a great time, and the next day it was up to me to show her whatever Shweta couldn't. First, I took Hinna to Juhu beach. We told the driver to meet us at the other end as we took a nice little stroll down the beach. As we were walking, she was telling about what her friends thought of me. I had never been given so many compliments I think. I had definitely passed the test, and how. Walking on the beach with Hinna felt like right out of a Bollywood movie. If I were to tell her the same, she would have married me right then and there. Her affliction to Bollywood was just amazing.

Considering this, the next place I took her to in Mumbai had to be Shah Rukh Khan's mansion. She was elated, and later suggested coffee at The Taj, her favorite place in all of India. It was like striking off things from her to-do list in Mumbai, and I was happy I was with her while she was doing that. At the Taj, we had this conversation about if we thought we were perfect for each other. I knew she was perfect for me. As a matter of fact, I knew she was perfect for me within a month of talking to her. But I didn't tell her that. Instead I told her that I usually take more time to decide on such important things. I should have just put an 'I am Stupid' sticker right across my forehead. She went the other way and told me that she thought I would definitely make her happy, and that she would definitely consider getting married to me. Why in the world I was not taking this opportunity to just hold her hand and tell her how madly in love I was with her? I still held up my macho image and told her that I would answer this question once I was ready to.

From there, we took a stroll down Bandstand. The climate was really nice and pleasant. Of course, along with Bandstand, I introduced her to a different side of Mumbai as well. Sitting right next to each other on the rocks were hundreds of couples. If one person from a pair stretched their arm out, they would hit the adjacent pair. I have never seen more romantic people, in such romantic settings in my life than people from Mumbai. We had to get out of the romantic spot soon as we were to catch a late show the new blockbuster 3 Idiots with Shweta and her mother. Hinna was surprised that we had to stand up for the national anthem before the show. It is a bit weird for people new to the city as to why they would play the national anthem before movies. This is definitely not how to promote patriotism. But then I am sure it is not the worst idea anyone has ever come up with. The movie was pretty good, and was based on Chetan Bhagat's book 5 Point Someone. The only problem with the movie, like my friend Prasad put it, was that Aamir Khan forgot that he was no longer dyslexic after Taarein Zameen Par.

The following day, I went over to meet Hinna quite early. We had planned to go to Elephanta Caves. She also wanted to travel by the local trains. We travelled in the first class compartment upon her insistence, and I wouldn't blame her for it considering the sheer number of people crammed up in the second-class compartments during rush hours. We reached Churchgate station and I had no clue how to get to the Gateway of India from where we would take the ferry to the caves. Hinna just smiled and said that she had been around that area a couple of days back with Shweta, and that she kind of knew where to go. Within 15-20 minutes we were standing right outside the Gateway of India. How amazing was this woman?

We took tickets and sat on a ferry which looked like it could capsize at any moment. The waves were just rocking the chair like one of those rides at Esselworld. I figured the ferry ride to be about half-an-hour but it took about an hour to get there. By the time we reached, both of us were so exhausted that we really didn't feel like doing anything. But considering we had taken so much trouble to get there, we decided to go ahead with it anyway. Before reaching the caves, we had to climb about a hundred steps to get to the top which was even more tiring. However, finally after about 2 hours since leaving home, we had reached Elephanta Caves. There were about 6 caves, each cave being about a few feet from each other. The first one was the main attraction, with breathtaking sculptures. We spend a good half-an-hour to explore the whole cave. The rest of the caves were pretty boring, and seemed like they were just made to attract tourists. But spending time with Hinna in such places was also fun. We sat down on the steps to one of the caves and started listening to Hindi music. She loved Hindi songs, and made me listen to it a lot too. The best part about listening to these songs from her iPhone was sitting close to her and putting our heads together. It felt really good; filmy but good.

By the time we got back to civilization to the Gateway of India, it was almost 6pm. We quickly caught the train back and got off at Santacruz as I had promised her that I would show her where I lived. We decided to grab something to eat first from a Chinese restaurant and headed home. She looked at all the trophies I had got and was surprised my brother was never jealous. Truth be told, I was the one who was always jealous of him. I really wanted to be like him because he was always so cool. Sitting there in my living room, I noticed how cute she was looking that day. She had adorned a sleeveless blue top, with blue jeans, and had her sunglasses in her hair to hold it back. I wanted to just sit there and stare at her like a stalker. However, in some time, we decided it was best to get her to Shweta's house, where she was living, before it got too late.

Hinna was supposed to leave the next evening. We met up for coffee early and went to Crosswords to buy her a book. Shweta's mom had invited me over for lunch as well so we headed back there. Shweta's mom had made some amazing seafood and Hinna and I could not stop eating. I must have finished more than half of what the poor lady had cooked for us. After lunch, we all sat down chatting for a bit before it was time for Hinna to leave for the airport. Unfortunately, Shweta's mom decided to come with us to the airport as well. Once we reached the airport, we said our goodbyes. I could not even hug Hinna as Shweta's mom was around. After Hinna went into the airport, and Shweta's mom left, I waited outside looking for rickshaws to take me home. But suddenly, my phone started ringing at it was Hinna. I thought she might have forgotten something and picked up to check what was wrong. All I heard on the phone was, "Turn around."

I turned around to see her coming out towards me. As she came close, I just took her into my arms. Everyone around was looking at us. Men were looking at the free display of affections, while old ladies disgusted at how we could hug in a public place. But I was not going to let anyone deter me from holding her in my arms. It felt so good. I didn't want to let her go. Like a fool, I again refrained from telling her anything. If only I had a ring, I would have gone down on one knee right then and there. I finally let her go, and though we were both not sure when and where we would meet again as I would be heading out to Boston and she would be going to Denver, I assured her that we would meet again. I was not sure how it was going to happen either, but how could I not meet my *Punjaban*?

The next day was New Years and Rehan and I had decided to go to NSCI in Worli to bring the New Year in. Rehan had called me after a year and a half when I was in Colorado and we had started talking again. Everything was back to normal and we had cleared everything out between us. He reached Mumbai on the 31st itself and we decided to go to this place as a school friend of mine had brought tickets for the place. We reached there to find out that it was officially the lamest New Year party ever with old people sitting and having food, while kids were running around the dance floor. My school friend's boss was an obnoxious idiot who could have naturally made the cast of 3 idiots. Rehan and I were really bored there and soon enough left for a house party. As our luck had it, the house party wasn't that great either. The people there seemed to be having a good time but we didn't know anyone, and so yet again we were on the road. We ended up at some bar and ended up drinking till early morning.

In the next few days, my mom was taken to the hospital a couple of times as the pain in her arm had escalated. The doctors suggested the pain might just go away with some pain killers, and this time they gave some really strong ones like morphine. At the hospital, my mother seemed ok having such heavy medications, though her memory seemed a bit hazy. However, once she was discharged and we reached home, things really took a turn for the worse. The drugs were really affecting her, and she was in a semi-conscious state. SO much so that the poor thing could not even get up to go to the restroom. I am no believer, but God forbid anyone having to see their mothers in a similar state. We had to get her admitted quickly. I ran to find us a cab. None of the cab guys were ready to come to a hospital. That's the great thing about India. Taxi and rickshaw drivers, who are supposed to take you wherever you want to go and as a rule cannot refuse, blatantly refuse your request. As a matter of fact, we have to beg these guys to take us somewhere. Luckily one taxi guy came with me, himself complaining how any taxi can refuse going to a hospital. I reached home and my dad, a family friend and I had to seat my mother on a chair and carry her down. She could not even keep her feet on the chair as they dragged from one step to the other. Could I really leave my folks alone at such a stage and go back in 2 weeks time?

We admitted her at the hospital and waited for her to recover a bit. As she was unable to breathe properly, she was shifted to the ICU. Dad and I decided to take turns in sitting at the hospital. My dad would feed my mom breakfast and lunch. Right after lunch, I would get to the hospital, feed my mom some snacks and give her tea in the evening, and then leave after my dad came back late in the evening. As Rehan was in town as well, I would leave the hospital, go home and change, and then head out to meet him. Meeting him was a good way to keep my mind of what was happening in the hospital. In all this running around, the time I spent on the phone talking to Hinna also reduced. I could have easily postponed my plans with Rehan for an hour or so but for some reason I never did. I would end up talking to her for a maximum of half-an-hour a day. After a few days, she really got frustrated with me and went on the trip she had told me about to Jhansi with Ankit and a few others. At this time, I had no problems with this guy. Things were going great guns with Hinna and nothing could have come close to breaking us up.

I could not get through to Hinna for the next few days. I was not insecure or something about her being with Ankit in any way but at the same time I wanted to talk to her. It just felt really weird not being able to talk to her for so long. I kept my days busy with the hospital and going out with Rehan but she was always there at the back of my mind. My mom was moved to the general ward soon which was definitely a relief. However, I was discussing not going back to the US in Jan, and to defer my admission till fall with my brother and my uncle in Dubai*. I could not talk to my dad regarding the same as he would have not even heard my side and just would have rejected the idea. The day before I was to leave, I was sitting at the hospital while my mom was sound sleep. Suddenly she shrieked, and her whole body started shaking. She was having a seizure. I rushed to call the nurses and the doctor. They took about 15 minutes to stabilize her, but she was still distorted and had no idea what was going on. She did not even remember what happened in the last half-an-hour. Her lip was bleeding badly as she had bitten it hard while she got the seizure. There was no way in hell I was going back at this point, leaving my folks alone.

My dad came to the hospital in a few hours and I told him what had happened. I also told him about postponing my return till August. Though he rejected the idea at first, I was

*Do I need to say anything about me, a Malayali, having a relative in Dubai?

adamant and told him that I just could not leave considering the situation. He thought for a while and asked me to do what I felt was right. I knew I was taking the right decision by staying back. It would set back my studies, and as a result my career, by about 6 months or so but my family needed me at this point. I finally got through to Hinna before I cancelled my tickets. I told her what I had planned. She was very supportive and even helped me in the cancellation of the tickets. However, since then things changed a lot between us.

We hadn't spoken for around 3-4 days and ever since she got back, our talk time had reduced considerably. Things seemed fine between us but that spark that was there at first seemed missing. She filled me in on what she was up to for the few days we hadn't spoken but also said she had a harmless crush on Ankit's brother. I understand harmless crushes and they are fine, but the problem was she was going to spend the next whole week with them, while I was left with nothing but phone conversations. Now the insecurities started to creep in. I would never bother anyone even if I was insecure. Soniya gave me a good enough ride on the insecurity rollercoaster. However, I definitely started making more efforts to talk to Hinna more often in the day. She was as sweet as ever and would talk to me whenever I called. But at the end of the day, she would go out and hang out with these people, one guy who was obsessed with marrying her, and his brother on whom she had a harmless crush. I needed to book myself a ticket to Delhi asap.

Making a trip to Delhi was obviously out of question. My staying back would have been useless if I was not around my family. A couple of days before she was to leave, Hinna called me late in the night and we spoke for about an hour and half. We discussed how things are going to be difficult with me being here and her in Denver, and how long distance relationships are senseless. I was very honest and told her that I really wanted to be in a relationship with her, and that I wanted to ask her out, but again the timing was just off. I finally even had the courage to tell her yes to the question she had asked at Taj. A few times while I was with Rehan, after having a few drinks, I had messaged Hinna telling her some things which really showed how I felt about her. Alcohol always gives me courage. But again why would a girl want to be with someone who can only be intimate after being a few drinks down? As result of me blurting out such things via messages, I got the feeling she didn't believe whatever I said via phone that night either. We agreed in the end that we will still date each other and see where life takes us.

Hinna left in a couple of days, and I was left wondering how things would turn out. Soon, I got good news that my mother was being discharged after almost a month of being bedridden at the hospital. I didn't know if it was a good thing because there had been a relapse after the initial treatment, which meant more chemotherapy. They had finished the first session of chemo for this cycle, and the next was due in 21 days and so my mother was being discharged. She seemed way better than when we had admitted her. Though she was still a bit weak, the improvement was significant, and she could talk properly without slurring. We took her home, and the delight to be back home after so long was quite evident on her face. I was happy to see her smile after ages.

As I was going to be in India for a few months, I decided to start looking for jobs. I really didn't want to be a leach and live off my parents for the time I was home. Prasad, my friend from the SNFT group, told me that his company was looking for someone for business development, and as I had done something similar before I left to be one of the PIGS, I volunteered and soon started working. Working with someone from the SNFT group meant one thing, drinking like crazy every weekend. Now that my mom was back home, I could afford to come home late on weekends as I did not have to go to the hospital early the next day. We started going out on weekends, and getting hammered. They all blamed me for the increase in drinking sessions. Apparently, the time I was away, the sessions had reduced. I was in no way to be blamed for this sudden increase in consumption of alcoholic beverages. I had even suggested that we drink biweekly. However, my suggestion was misinterpreted a bit and instead of drinking once in two weeks, they started drinking twice a week.

One Saturday, we all decided to go to Catholic Gymkhana for a few drinks. Our usual routine was to sit at home and have something but this time everyone wanted to step out. Jojo had a membership at the Gymkhana and so he signed everyone in. We started drinking and soon enough there was chaos. One girl who was with us but I had met for the first time was telling us how money was not everything. I am sorry but I really believe money is everything. What is there that money cannot get you? If I had a lot of money, I would have provided the best treatment for my mother. If I had a lot of money, I could be next to Hinna at that time. And get her back with me if I had enough money for us to live for the rest of our lives. How can money not give you everything that you want?

I also noticed there was a girl sitting at a table at the other corner who kept looking at me. I liked the attention alright but she was doing it while she was holding her boyfriend's hand! She kept staring at me the whole night. I was a bit scared because I was in no condition to fight anyone and the way she was staring, if her boyfriend noticed it even once, he would have come to argue. Not that I was at fault, but that's how we Indian men are. We never believe that our women can ever be at fault. If she is staring, it has to be because the guy is giving her "dirty" looks. Luckily, those people left sooner than later. But right after they left, this big group of "uncles" and "aunties" came, and there was an elderly Asian woman totally trying to grab my attention. It was freakier than watching Ozzy biting off a bat's head. Thankfully, we were all drunk enough and decided to retire early. Abu had called for a driver as he was sure he couldn't drive. On our way back home, Prasad started off his usual conversation with the driver. You see, Prasad is notorious for having conversations about birth control measures with rickshaw guys and taxi drivers. He had once famously taken out a chocolate flavored condom from his wallet and had handed it to the rickshaw driver because he had no clue what a condom was. Sex education of a different kind I suppose. Our driver too was oblivious to the existence of something called a condom and for the half-an-hour drive got a good enough sex education lecture.

Since the time Hinna had left, I hadn't spoken to her. I

had met her online on Facebook once, and she had told me she wanted to talk to me. I knew this was The Talk, the talk before breaking up with someone. I tried calling her a few times but the couple of times she managed to pick up she was busy and could not talk. I felt like she was ignoring my calls the same way she used to ignore Ankit's when she was in Mumbai. I felt more and more anxious with every passing day. Finally, she called me one fine evening. We had some small talk but my anxiety got the better of me and I quickly asked her what she wanted to talk to me about. She said she didn't want to beat around the bush and told me that she wanted to talk to me about two things. First of all, she said that we shouldn't be dating as it was impractical. And secondly, she said that Ankit had asked her to marry him and she was considering it. It felt like someone had ripped out my heart and thrown it into a swamp in Florida where a couple of alligators grabbed it at each end and went into the death roll. Though I was kind of expecting it, as is always the case with everyone, there was a small voice that kept telling me everything was going to be fine; but it wasn't. I was speechless. All I could come up with was, "But I thought you hated that guy." She went on to tell me how they had come close the last few weeks in Delhi. After she was done, all I could tell her was I could not talk to her any more. There was no way I could only be friends with a girl I was absolutely in love with.

I kept thinking to myself what went wrong. But it was very evident what had gone wrong. It was me who never committing. My fear always held back my feelings, and she wanted to know what I felt. How could I expect her to hang around forever without knowing if it meant anything to me? I had driven off women before, sometimes on purpose and sometimes accidentally, by coming on too strong. Now it was me driving off one woman that actually meant something but not saying anything. The worst part was that since that conversation, every time I saw or heard anything about Delhi or New York it would remind me of her. Bollywood songs were a strict no-no too, especially this one particular song from the new movie Ishqiyan, which she had up on her Facebook and Ankit had 'liked' it. I even had to take her off the networking website because I could not bare the sight of her commenting on Ankit or his brother's photos. Considering everything that was going on in my life, my mom, Hinna, my career, all I could think of was this old Hindi adage: *Jab naseeb hi g***u, toh kya karega pandu.*

Now when I look back on my life, I realize that I have done nothing significant. Academically, I may be more qualified than a lot of people. But is it what I really want? I did engineering thinking everyone was doing it, so should I. I went to the US because everyone was doing it. When will I ever think what I want? Doing engineering was fine, but going to the US has a lot of investment in it. It is a risk you should be taking only if you really want to do it. I say this to all the future PIGS out there; do not go to the US just because everyone else is. If you decide to go, don't base your school on your girlfriend, or where your friends are, or where your counselor told you to apply. No matter what your academic scores are, no matter what your GRE scores are, apply to good schools only i.e. top 20 schools. If you don't get into them, then don't go, and I say this with experience. I am not saying everyone who goes to bad schools ends up jobless, but how many of them are actually happy with what they are doing? Most of them join the Indian consulting firms and does stuff they didn't even learn in graduate school. Follow your heart, not the crowd.

Thinking about how there are no high points in my life right now, I should take the easy way out as most Mumbai students were doing some time back; suicide*. But I am not that weak. I am not even going to think of suicide like all these idiots who kill themselves just because their teacher scolded them in front of the class. I am way too strong for that. I will get my life straight and I will go back to the US after my mom is in the pink of her health, to make a name for myself. On second thought, naaahh! I think I would rather go with plan B of getting fatter by around 30 kilos, growing a moustache and entering South Indian movies.

---

*I am really amazed at the number of students that committed suicide in Mumbai. If you really wanted to die, you just had to go to Australia. They were killing us for free anyway!

ANECDOTE : GAME, SET, MATCH MIRZA.

Sania Mirza broke up with her childhood friend, Sohrab Mirza as the guy and his family did not want Sania to be a tennis player after marriage as it would keep her away from home for a long time, and instead wanted her to be a homemaker. Sohrab, I don't know how much you liked Sania but if you really liked her and followed her performance in tournaments, you would never ever let her go. There was no question of her staying away from home for too long anyway considering she loses in the first or second round every tournament!

If anyone of the writers is interested in publishing a book with
Expression publication then he/she is welcome.
For further details visit our website
www.expressionpublications.com.
Or write into us at -
Expression publications
E-mail id- expressionpublications@yahoo.co.in

Books published by - Expression Publications.

1. Oh Shit Not Again! – By Mandar Kokate. - *A National Bestseller.*

2. Love Lust & Life – By Azhan Ahsan. - *A National Bestseller.*

3. I am Papa – By Pranav Bhattacharya.

4. Manage Time Manage Life - By H.S.Gopalan.

5. When the Marriage is made in 'COMEDY CIRCUS' – By Deepali Basur.

6. Life Un-plugged – by Bhavya Sharma.